OW

GREAT
ORMOND
STREET

GREAT ORMOND STREET

BEHIND THE SCENES AT THE WORLD'S MOST FAMOUS CHILDREN'S HOSPITAL

ACCOMPANIES THE BBC TELEVISION SERIES

Alan Sleator and Denise Winn

EBURY PRESS

LONDON

First published in 1996

1 3 5 7 9 10 8 6 4 2

First published in the United Kingdom in 1996 by Ebury Press
Random House, 20 Vauxhall Bridge Road, London SW1V 2SA

Random House Australia (Pty) Limited
20 Alfred Street, Milsons Point, Sydney,
New South Wales 2061, Australia

Random House New Zealand Limited
18 Poland Road, Glenfield
Auckland 10, New Zealand

Random House South Africa (Pty) Limited
PO Box 337, Bergvlei, South Africa

Random House UK Limited Reg. No. 954009

A catalogue record for this book is available from the British Library

ISBN: 0 09 181398 0

Editors: Margot Richardson, Nicky Thompson
Designer: Jerry Goldie

Printed and bound in Great Britain by Butler & Tanner Ltd,
Frome and London

Papers used by Ebury Press are natural recyclable products made from
wood grown in sustainable forests.

CONTENTS

INTRODUCTION

Great Ormond Street Children's Hospital was the first opened specifically for young patients in the United Kingdom. It is now the most famous children's hospital in the world, and has provided inspiration and guidance for many similar institutions in other countries.

Right: The first purpose-built hospital building in Great Ormond Street opened in 1875.

Far right: The modern entrance to the new Variety Club Building.

Although such a facility for sick children is taken almost for granted these days, the welfare of children was not always quite so well catered for.

The hospital was opened on St Valentine's Day, 14th February, 1852. This was in response to a lack of almost any specialist medical care for children, and appalling levels of child deaths. About ten years earlier, statistics show that of all the patients in London hospitals, less than 6 per cent were children, yet children made up half of the 50,000 people who died in London every year. This was a time when malnutrition, tuberculosis and rickets were rife and only half of those born reached adulthood. Clearly there was a pressing need for an urgent improvement in children's health, and for a hospital to focus on their particular needs.

Great Ormond Street was founded by Dr Charles West, and started with ten beds. From this modest beginning the hospital has grown to offer the widest range of paediatric expertise under one roof in the whole of Britain. But there were times during its early years when its future looked uncertain, sometimes from a lack of funds. Queen Victoria was an early supporter, while Charles Dickens, by writing and public speaking, significantly boosted both its reputation and fundraising capability.

Above: Dr Charles West, founder of the first hospital specifically dedicated to children.

Right: An early Christmas at the hospital.

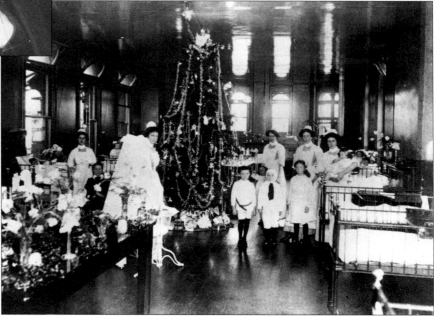

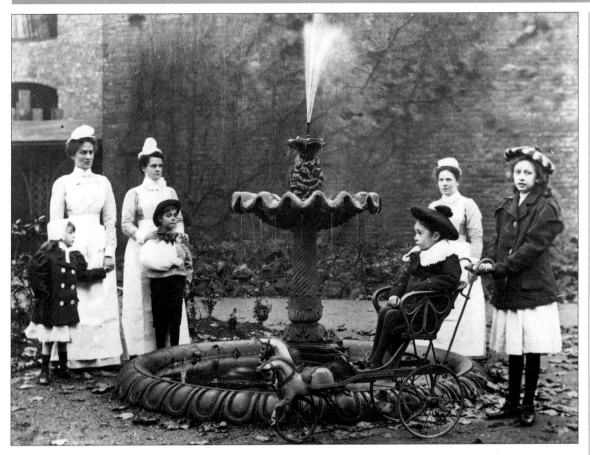

The famous wishing well in 1905.

The hospital first expanded by buying the house next door, and then by building new premises, opened in 1875, which had room for over 100 beds. Most recently, in February 1994, the new Variety Club Building was opened, housing the most up-to-date paediatric facilities in Europe. This building was funded by the Wishing Well Appeal, a huge fundraising effort which raised £54 million from the public, both in Britain and abroad. The appeal was named after the fountain that originally stood in the hospital garden, where children would throw coins and wish for good health.

With over 300 beds, Great Ormond Street Children's Hospital is now one of the world's leading children's hospitals. Children come from all over Britain, and the rest of the world, to take advantage of its 32 different clinical and surgical specialities. They are cared for, not only by paediatric doctors and nurses but also by highly dedicated dietitians, pharmacists, radiologists and many more experts in their fields. The hospital has the country's largest paediatric intensive care unit and runs the biggest neonatal surgery programme.

Each year Great Ormond Street welcomes more than 18,000 children as inpatients and sees nearly four times that figure as outpatients. The children referred here are often in need of treatment for the rarest, most complex and life-threatening conditions. Some may need to see as many as 12 different teams of specialists, and some stay for as long as two years. Many come back to the hospital for treatment throughout their childhood – and even when they are adults.

There is a sense of innovation and pioneering that becomes apparent to anyone who gets involved in the medical side of the hospital. Working alongside clinicians are 200 scientists at the Institute of Child Health, the hospital's research arm, which is connected to the hospital. Their research work involves investigating the causes and finding cures for a wide range of children's illnesses. For example, one research team is leading the field in identifying children at risk of heart disease. Another has recently discovered the gene responsible for Crouzon Syndrome – a rare cranio-facial disorder that affects the structure of the head and face – perhaps paving the way to finding the means to prevent children from undergoing complicated surgery.

Other new techniques include cochlear implants, enabling previously deaf children to hear; epilepsy surgery for children who suffer severe seizures; and gene therapy.

The hospital also runs a large training programme, currently with 468 student paediatric nurses who are trained in partnership with South Bank University.

SERVICES AT GREAT ORMOND STREET

Total number of beds: 305

Average bed occupancy per year: 74 per cent

Number of wards: 25

Operating theatres in use: 6

Operations per year: 8,035

Number of intensive care beds: 31 (15 cardiac, 11 paediatric, 5 neonatal), plus 5 high-dependency beds

Throughout the hospital, the family is regarded as being vitally important. Parents are encouraged to be involved in their child's care and an extensive range of services is offered to address a family's emotional, spiritual and social needs. There is a play centre for patients, their brothers and sisters; a play specialist on every ward; a hospital radio station, a school and a family dining room. A variety of accommodation is available for mothers or fathers to stay overnight, or for long periods, near to their child. Parents can also talk to qualified counsellors, and the hospital's chapel welcomes people of all faiths.

In April 1994, the hospital became an NHS Trust and under new funding arrangements is now part of the health service internal market. While the NHS pays for the day-to-day running of the hospital, the Special Trustees of Great Ormond

Street Children's Hospital aim to raise an additional £10 million each year to provide family support services, buy the best in new equipment and help with even more research.

Great Ormond Street is a place of hope for sick children and their parents. It offers help to the helpless, treating children with the rarest conditions, from all over Britain, and indeed the world, regardless of class or creed. Although the children are often described as brave, it is also a bravery borne out of having no option, and the hospital offers a chance to reclaim their childhood and look to the future with optimism.

Many of the children and parents featured in the following pages are those who appear in the BBC Television series *Great Ormond Street*. This is a further account of the treatment they – and others – received, how they felt about it and their hopes for the future. It is also an explanation of just some of the wide range of work done by the hospital, told through the eyes of the people who work there and the families who come to them for help.

Princess Diana, president of the hospital, opened the Variety Club Building on the hospital's 142nd birthday. Here she chats to patients Hannah Eiseman-Renyard and Eleanor Corrigan.

THE PLACE AND THE PEOPLE WHO WORK THERE

Walk in through the sliding glass doors of Great Ormond Street's reception area and the first thing you see is a big red shiny bus. It's usually covered with children scrambling to sit in the driver's seat. It's such a bright, happy and colourful focus point you'd be forgiven for thinking you'd come to the wrong place. This doesn't look, sound or even smell like a hospital.

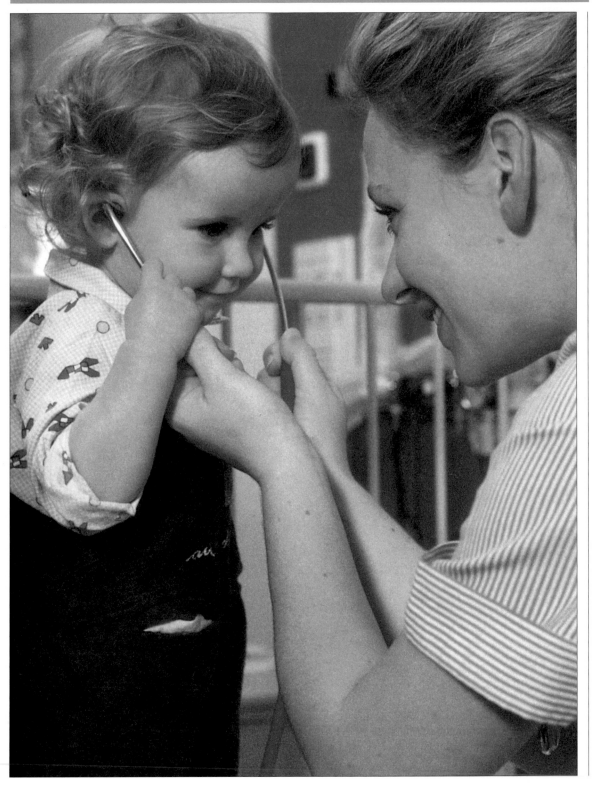

A FRIENDLY RECEPTION

When parents, children and visitors come to Great Ormond Street Children's Hospital, often the first person they meet is volunteer William Gates. Mr Gates is one of about 250 unpaid workers who has made a regular commitment to the hospital. He works closely with staff at the main reception desk, and guides visitors to various departments and wards around the labyrinth of buildings that make up the hospital.

'I show them the way to where they want to go,' he says. 'It could be anywhere – X-ray, wards, supplies . . . It took ages at first to work out where all the wards were and I used to worry that I'd get it wrong. I reckon it took a good nine months to really get to know my way around thoroughly.

'But this job is much more than acting as a guide. I get on very well with children and this aspect of the work I find very rewarding. I try to build up a rapport with them. I usually ask them which football team they support then tell them that, secretly, I support Chelsea. This usually works.'

St Christopher's Chapel had to be moved to fit into the new building. The entire structure was slid about 100 ft along a purpose-built runway.

THE SURROUNDINGS

It is not surprising the people who come to visit and to work at Great Ormond Street take a while to get oriented. The hospital complex includes 25 wards; a large outpatients department on two floors; a shop; a cafeteria; six operating theatres; recovery areas; seminar rooms connected by television monitors to the theatres; staff rooms and numerous offices; a sterilisation and disinfection unit; play areas on each ward; a school; a radio station; a quiet room; and a beautiful nineteenth-century chapel. There are also facilities for dispensing medicines, X-rays, physiotherapy, psychology, counselling and practical support.

All this is contained in three main buildings: the Southwood Building that dates back to the 1930s, the new Variety Club Building that was opened in 1994 and the Cardiac wing built 20 years ago. Each floor of the Variety Club Building has a theme, from transport on the ground floor to safari country on the top floor, where lions and tigers appear on curtains, wall friezes and floor tiles and parents staying overnight sleep under safari-themed covers. By the hospital's pharmacy there is a huge mural depicting the story of Peter Pan, which has special significance for the hospital (see Chapter 11).

Despite all the different departments – and the fact that more than 2,000 people work there – Great Ormond Street feels surprisingly small. Some consultants based in older parts of the hospital, often leaders in their fields, share offices just big enough for two chairs with other colleagues. Papers and files spill out of cupboards never designed for such loads, and vital research statistics are often topped by an electric kettle – the quickest way to get a decent cup of tea. Yet in these small rooms lie the hopes of every parent who comes here.

NURSING

Nurses make up the largest working group at the hospital. There are more than 1,000, from 18-year-old trainees to highly qualified registered nurses with many years of experience.

Nurse training has altered radically in recent years. All the education – that is, the formal teaching as opposed to practical experience on the wards – has moved into universities, so that hospitals and academic institutions work together in partnership. Some students may come straight

Much of the decoration in the hospital is placed at child height, so it can be enjoyed to the full by the children it is intended for.

15

from school to do a three-year diploma in sick children's nursing; others may have already qualified in general adult nursing, but undertake further training to specialise in paediatrics gaining a degree, or even a master's. Further specialist courses are also available, including cardio-thoracic, oncology, intensive care, neurosciences, and caring for children with cystic fibrosis. But despite this new type of academic training, the actual practical care of sick children is still the top priority.

Another important development is the involvement of nurses in research. At the moment, almost all medical research is carried out by doctors, but there is an increasing trend for nurses and other staff, such as phsyiotherapists, to explore aspects of their work.

There are several research projects co-ordinated by nursing staff under way at Great Ormond Street. Angela Scarisbrick, Teaching Co-ordinator for the cardio-thoracic unit, is looking into incidence of pressure sores, which occur on the head, neck, nose and ears, experienced by infants and children undergoing cardiac surgery. These children seem to be more prone to these sores than other children in, for example, intensive care. It is not known why this happens, but is thought that it may have something to do with long periods on bypass during surgery. Obviously, finding the cause could help prevent or minimise them.

Another study, co-ordinated by Martha Worrell, the Night Co-ordinator, is researching the relationship and dynamics between nurses, children and parents, and what happens to the nurses themselves, especially under stressful conditions such as bereavement.

STAFF

Total staff employed: 1760
Number of consultants: 135
Junior doctors: 101
Registered nurses and healthcare assistants: 646
Other scientific and professional staff: 312
Managerial, administrative and clerical staff: 438
Ancillary staff (including cooks, porters and manual): 128

Unpaid volunteers: approx 250
Student paediatric nurses: 468

FURTHER SUPPORT

It is not just medical matters that are considered important. Great Ormond Street Hospital has a large complement of social workers and counsellors. Their prime task is to help parents to come to terms with their child's illness and the implications surrounding it.

Social workers also help families with the practical side of life when their child comes to Great Ormond Street. They may be able to offer advice and help with a range of things from travel arrangements and train fares to organising accommodation and care for other children. In short, while the doctors and nurses look after the children, a major part of the social worker's role is to look after and help their families.

BEHIND THE SCENES

There are numerous other jobs that are vital for the efficient functioning of the hospital, many of which are more important than they might at first appear.

An army of cleaners is always at work all over the building; the actual standard of cleanliness is often a vital part of the medical process. For example, children with immune deficiencies (such as Joshua in Chapter 5) may have to spend periods in sterile surroundings. The smallest deposit of dust, carelessly left behind, could harbour harmful bacteria.

When you consider the amount of machinery and equipment used in a hospital – from life-support systems to basic heating – the role of engineers and maintenance workers is also essential. Steve Saunders is a technician in Plant and Operations Maintenance. His job involves the hospital's monitor control system: a vast computer network that keeps an eye on areas such as security, heating, temperatures in the blood banks and electrical supplies to life-support equipment. If any of these systems do not function as they should, the computer network alerts the technicians (or the hospital switchboard, out of hours) and an engineer can be called to rectify the problem.

And providing food for families and staff is also a vital service. Lizzie Hand is the hospital's catering manager, in charge of all the catering staff, purchasing supplies, arranging menus and monitoring food quality.

'We supply the Peter Pan cafe near the outpatients department, the staff dining room and the wards,' she says. 'That means feeding about 1500 people with an average of two meals per day, from 7am to 8pm, seven days a week. We get through about 720 loaves of bread per week, and 2,800 pints of milk – that's nearly 150,000 pints a year!'

Lizzie Hand's catering department is responsible for preparing over 20,000 meals a week – yet there is still time to do its own baking.

THE INSTITUTE OF CHILD HEALTH

As medical research and successful treatment go hand in hand, investigation into children's illnesses is a vitally important area. The Institute of Child Health was officially set up in 1945, with four cubicles in a ward of the hospital. Today it is the largest paediatric research centre in Britain, with an annual budget of over £15 million. It employs more than 400 people, with 21 professorships and about 130 PhD students at any one time. It also offers a comprehensive teaching programme in many areas of child health for healthcare professionals, and each year several thousand students attend over 50 short courses.

Although the ICH is concerned primarily with research, it is inextricably linked with the hospital. Many of the consultants who are actively treating patients are also involved in research programmes. For example, Dr John Deanfield, who specialises in the treatment of heart disease, is also co-ordinating research on detecting the early signs of future heart disease in children (see Chapter 7).

A further area of the Institute's work lies abroad. One example of this involves nutritional studies in Bangladesh, investigating how the amount of iodine received by women during pregnancy can affect the mental and physical wellbeing of their children. The results of the research have been passed on to the Bangladeshi government.

Machinery and services are monitored round the clock to make sure all the systems are operating correctly.

KEEPING PEOPLE HAPPY

Children love to play, and play is considered an important part of life at Great Ormond Street. There are 37 play specialists in the hospital, whose role is not only to entertain and supervise the children but often – with the help of a long-suffering teddy bear – to explain what is happening to them, or the procedures they are about to undergo.

The hospital also has its own radio station, known as Radio GOSH, run entirely by volunteers. It broadcasts on two evenings and all day Sunday from a room on the top floor. Children can take part in competitions, make requests, and are welcome to visit the studio. From time to time there are celebrity guests. In the past these have included comedian Robin Williams and pop stars Right Said Fred.

Other volunteers who visit the hospital include Sandra Stone. Sandra was the principal of a nursery school for 21 years, but now works in pet therapy, bringing animals into the hospital play centre, and the wards, to visit the children. Several species have been used: dogs, rabbits, guinea pigs and a chinchilla.

Obviously, the animals have to be carefully selected, both for excellent health (with constant veterinary checks) and a friendly disposition. 'I might even go so far as to say

---

INSTITUTE OF CHILD HEALTH RESEARCH THEMES

The institute has seven major areas of research:

- Inherited disease and congenital malformations
- The child in society
- Neurosciences and mental health
- Cardiorespiratory sciences and vascular biology
- Infection and immunity
- Cancer
- Nutrition

that they also need to be rather stoical and long-suffering,' she says. 'The first dog I introduced promptly took up residence in the Wendy house, and the rabbit and guinea pig soon had paint in their fur.'

The animals provide a welcome distraction from the hospital routine and provide a link with home and school. Sometimes, hospital role-play games are initiated. 'For example,' she explains, 'the dog was put to bed or had imaginary injuries bound up with bandages. Plastic meals were also prepared for her and I had to intervene only when she was expected to eat them!'

Sandra and the animals also visit the wards, including intensive care. Even with seriously ill children, the feeling of warm fur against a cheek can be interesting and comforting, and the attempts by a rabbit to chew a child's respirator tubes have been met with shrieks of laughter by the child.

Sandra Stone has found that rabbits and guinea pigs are the most suitable animals for hospital visits as they have a placid temperament – unlike hamsters, which are inclined to nip – and are the least likely small animals to transmit infections.

In fact, so convinced is Sandra of the therapeutic value of animals for sick children that she is in the process of setting up a charity (called CHATA – Children in Hospital and Animal Therapy Association) to extend this work.

'It's the atmosphere at Great Ormond Street which makes it so special,' says Alan Wilson, father of 14-year-old Neal who has had three heart operations there. (For more about Neal, see Chapter 7.)

'Our cardiologist makes you feel like you are the only people he is seeing that day.

'Neal has always been happy to be on a ward there because of the staff. Whenever he has had to come back in, the nurses laugh and say something light like, "What on earth are you doing back here again, Neal? You must really like the food."

'There's respect. When doctors talk to us about what's going on, they explain to Neal. We are very much sitting behind him and they don't look at us over the top of his head.

'There's always an undercurrent of humour which alleviates any tension. For something that is very serious Great Ormond Street is a very easy place to go to.'

THE PATIENTS

Great Ormond Street offers care to all age groups, from premature babies upwards. While 50 per cent of the patients are under two years old, others may attend up until the age of 16, or even older. Here are the stories of a just a few of these patients, showing the variety of expertise available at the hospital.

Great Ormond Street is known as a tertiary referral hospital. It does not have an Accident and Emergency department, and children are referred there from other places, to take advantage of the wide range of experts specialising in children's illnesses and to receive care for the rarest and most complex of diseases. Often, a child may be sent to Great Ormond Street because it has a particular area of expertise that has been developed or located there.

One such facility, for example, is a national centre for children with rheumatology problems, previously located at Northwick Park Hospital

in north London which has now moved to Great Ormond Street. Children being treated suffer mostly from Juvenile Chronic Arthritis (JCA), a painful condition which affects one in a thousand children.

DEBI

By the time three-and-a-half-year-old Debi, from Hatfield in Hertfordshire, had been diagnosed locally with JCA, her knees had fixed at a 35-degree angle, forcing her to get around indoors by shuffling along on her bottom and outside by sitting on her bike. She hadn't been able to walk for three months.

The first sign of Debi's condition was when she fell over and complained of a pain in her left knee. Instead of subsiding, the pain worsened and over the next five months spread to the other knee, her elbows and wrists. JCA is a difficult condition to diagnose, the diagnosis largely being arrived at by excluding other possibilities.

Like many children with this condition who are patients at the rheumatology centre, Debi will need physiotherapy every day of her childhood to exercise her joints and prevent the disease from taking further hold. But at first, it was a painful business to start straightening her legs and then building up her muscles.

Debi's knees were injected with steroids which immediately freed them up, allowing her to start bending and straightening them again. At night, she slept with splints to keep her knees straight. The morning after the injection was the first for five months on which she didn't wake up crying in pain.

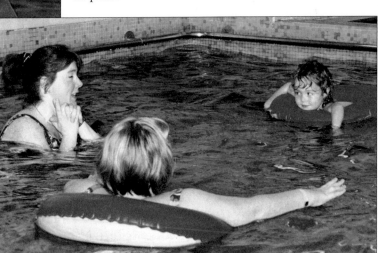

Once Debi was able to move more easily, she enjoyed exercise in the hydrotherapy pool – where water supports the body and allows it to move freely.

Once out of acute pain, little Debi could, for the first time, let physiotherapist Sue Maillard work on her legs and all her other joints. She also started to enjoy the hydrotherapy pool and to learn exercise routines to keep her mobile in the future.

ABIGAIL

Abigail Heath is a success story from another of the hospital's groundbreaking programmes. She is a lively three year old who knows that blowing loud raspberries is guaranteed to get her mum's hackles to rise, and consequently loves to tease by doing it. Yet a year ago Abigail wouldn't have had a clue what noise she was making or that she was making one at all: she was born profoundly deaf. Now, however, she has been given a sense of hearing, thanks to the cochlear implant programme which has been running for less than five years. It is a programme for children who have been born deaf rather than those who have had hearing and then lost it.

Abigail's inability to hear meant it was difficult for her to communicate – this had to be done through signing.

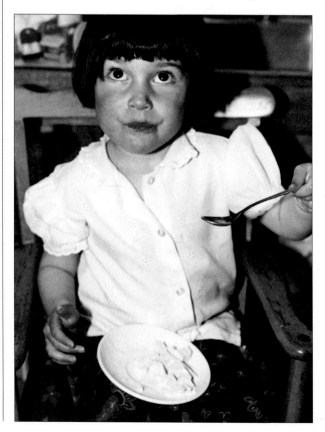

'We were very lucky that Abby was diagnosed so early,' says her mother, Lucy. 'Her hearing problem was picked up at her eight-month hearing test. I'm ashamed to say we hadn't noticed anything amiss ourselves because she was always so responsive and so vocal, which is very unusual for a deaf child.'

Over the next year Abigail was prescribed three different sets of hearing aids, each stronger than the last and each ineffective.

'We were desperate. Abby was very outgoing and could communicate in her own way but her language was limited and it was extremely hard to get information across to her. We were becoming deeply depressed because our options were running out,' says Lucy.

Early on Abigail had been referred to Great Ormond Street where, over a year, she was given all the tests and scans that could reveal a cause for her deafness.

'She had all the relevant bits in her ears. Everything was right except for the hair cells which were very badly damaged,' recalls Lucy. As a result of the tests, Abigail was offered a chance to have a cochlear implant. This is a small electronic device which is put into the head behind the ear. Outside the ear is a microphone and a speech processor which interpret sounds and turn them into electronic signals to stimulate the appropriate hearing nerve fibres. These in turn send messages on to the brain, giving a sensation of hearing.

To give a child the best chance of becoming accustomed to hearing sound and learning language, the implant operation needs to be carried out when young. For Abigail's parents it was crucial decision time. 'We had to weigh up whether it was better to let Abigail remain deaf and become part of the deaf community or to try to give her the chance of hearing, speaking and communicating in the way we do. In our hearts we knew we wanted her to have that chance, so we didn't spend a lot of time deciding,' says her mother, Lucy. 'The worst bit was our fear of anything going wrong.'

Insertion of a cochlear implant is quite a major operation, lasting over three hours and involving drilling into the inner ear, past the facial nerve. In the worst outcome, the facial nerve can be paralysed, causing a lopsided smile and impaired speech. 'In fact the doctors assured us things very rarely go wrong but that doesn't stop you jumping through hoops of course,' recalls Lucy. After the operation there is a wait of four weeks to let tissues settle and heal before a magnet is attached to the outside of the head and the processor is switched on.

Abigail was assessed over a period of nine months and then went forward for implant. On the day four weeks after the operation when 'switch on' was to occur, several family members, including her elder brother Joshua, were there.

'This was the moment when, if it had worked, Abby would hear for the first time all those insignificant little sounds in the room like a cough or a chair scraping. The processor was switched on and she responded instantly. The rest of the family got very emotional but Michael and I had been so stressed out, so desperately willing everything to be OK that we rather missed the emotion of the moment!

'For me, it all hit on the third day. Abby and I were walking down a hospital corridor on our way to the car and she kept zooming off too far in front. I just said to her, "Abby", quite softly. Her head jerked up at once

---

PATIENT INFORMATION

Inpatients per year (including private and overseas): 18,800
Outpatients per year: 66,000
Average length of stay: 6.3 days

Over half the patients need two or more specialists, of which nine per cent need more than five.

Children who are treated as outpatients can enjoy this colourful play area while they wait for their appointments.

and I knew she had heard. We got into the car, she fell asleep and I just sat there and howled!

'It has just gone from strength to strength since then. Even now when I speak at a normal pitch and she turns, I stand and gawk. Michael and I both still get very emotional.'

Abigail now goes to a school for nursery-age children with speech, language and hearing difficulties but her parents are fully expecting that she will be in a mainstream school when it is time to start proper full-time education. 'We know she will always need some help but we reckon she will be able to hold her own,' says Lucy.

Then she adds: 'But even if everything stopped here, and if nothing improved further, the implant has still been 100 per cent successful. We've all had such an uplift seeing the new enjoyment she is getting from her life. She's so much more a part of everything now.'

COLIN

Another patient who has been attending the hospital for almost all his life is Colin Newman who, since having a malignant tumour removed from his spine at the age of 18 months, has attended an oncology clinic at the hospital once a year for checks.

All was well until his last check, when he was 14. His parents, Philip and Maggie, pointed out a bulge on his back which was becoming more pronounced when he bent forward.

'He was also getting a degree of pain when he walked for any length of time and he was standing awkwardly,' says Philip. Doctors were concerned enough to send him for X-ray and refer him to consultant spinal surgeon, Mr Hillali Noordeen.

It was from him that the Newmans learned that, as a result of Colin's early cancer and treatment, there was a problem which was causing the bottom of his spine to kink. The spine was in danger of collapsing and, if it did, paralysis could result.

Mr Noordeen explained that an operation would be necessary. Surgery would be carried out through a cut in Colin's side. The lung would be moved gently out of the way so that he could reach the spine. He would then insert a tubular titanium cage which he would pack out with one of Colin's own ribs. The rib, because it was living bone, would gradually grow and fuse with Colin's spine while the cage would be held in place by a titanium plate screwed into the spine. Both the cage and the plate would remain there for the rest of his life.

With such major surgery, there is always the risk that the outcome might not be

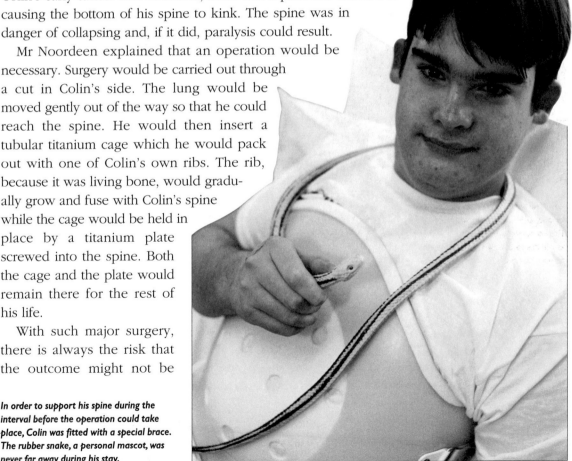

In order to support his spine during the interval before the operation could take place, Colin was fitted with a special brace. The rubber snake, a personal mascot, was never far away during his stay.

successful, or that some complication such as nerve damage might result, or that the structure inserted might be rejected. Anticipating the operation is a nerve-wracking time for both the child and the parents.

It was going to be high-intensity and high-stress surgery, especially as at one point the spinal cord would be exposed. A scan, carried out on the day before the operation, provided the very detailed pictures of his back required for the surgeon to work from. As it turned out, the surgery was trickier than even Mr Noordeen had expected because Colin's earlier cancer treatment with chemotherapy had affected the tissues.

Mr Hillali Noordeen, consultant spinal surgeon who operated on Colin's spine.

However, it was still a complete success. 'He is absolutely fine now,' says Philip. 'After his next check, six months on, we are expecting he will be told that there are no further limitations on him.' Colin was advised to walk and swim as much as possible but, alas not to ride a horse for a year; he is a very keen rider.

Colin's relationship with Great Ormond Street will continue for some time yet to ensure that he remains in good health. But in the meantime, he is looking forward eagerly to his first opportunity to go riding again.

LAUREN

Another regular visitor to the hospital is 13-year-old Lauren Ashley from Blunham in Bedfordshire. She plays clarinet in a county orchestra and tenor sax in a county band, an instrument that requires a particularly large amount of puff. Yet at 16 months old she had a tumour in one lung so large that it was pushing her other organs out of place, was given a one in ten chance of even surviving treatment and little likelihood of reaching the age of five.

Lauren was diagnosed with neuroblastoma, a very aggressive childhood cancer in which tumours can arise in many places in the body from cells that form the tissue of certain nerves. Lauren had had very few warning symptoms, yet by the time she was diagnosed she had not only the tumour in her lung but secondary tumours in her bone and bone marrow. There are four stages signifying degree of spread in neuroblastoma and Lauren was already in stage IV, which was why her prospects of cure were so very low.

'By the time we received the diagnosis, Lauren was within days of dying,' recalls her mother, Shelagh. 'It was an unbelievable shock. The doctors at Great Ormond Street explained everything very gently but in complete detail, so we weren't left in any doubt of her extremely slim chances of survival.'

Nine days earlier Shelagh had taken Lauren to her GP because she was oddly lethargic and her breathing was laboured. As Lauren's elder sister Holly had asthma, the GP assumed Lauren was suffering the same and wanted to put her on a nebuliser. But as the surgery's nebuliser was out on loan she was obliged to ask if Lauren could use the nebuliser in the local hospital's casualty department. So began the chain of events that led so swiftly to Great Ormond Street and that slim chance of life. The casualty doctor realised Lauren had fluid on her lung and admitted her. Her lung was drained several times and each time the fluid was found to be full of blood. Tests were inconclusive and it was after transfer to Great Ormond Street that the grim diagnosis was finally made.

'My husband's nephew had died only three months before of a spinal tumour, so cancer was very much in our minds at that moment. To have it happen twice within the same family in so short a time was just devastating,' says Shelagh.

Shelagh and husband Peter were asked if they even wanted to put Lauren through the treatment because it was so unpleasant. 'But there was no question in my mind,' says Shelagh. 'Lauren was such a tough toddler, so spirited, such a handful. I thought, "one child in ten makes it and I'm sure that child is Lauren." After the shock and when we'd had time to take everything in, I just knew she was going to be OK.'

Once the diagnosis had been made, Lauren was moved to the cancer ward. 'We were told we would feel more at home in it because all the children there had cancer. I thought, "I don't want to feel at home there!" I thought it would be miserable and depressing,' remembers Shelagh. 'But it was the most optimistic, cheerful place. People laughed and joked and at first that shocked me, until I realised that was the way to cope. The nurses were lovely and played with the children. It was mostly a really happy place.'

Lauren has now completely recovered, and leads a busy and very active life.

From the outset Lauren defied all expectations of her. As the tumour in the lung was so large, it was anticipated that she would need to stay in hospital for two sessions of aggressive chemotherapy three weeks apart before she could go home and continue treatment on an outpatient basis.

But she responded so well to the first session that she was able to go home.

She had to have nine sessions of four-day chemotherapy with four different drugs and the drug given on the second day always made her violently sick. 'But once she had started to pick up, she even took that in her stride. We tried to make a joke of it and treat it as normal. The doctors and nurses were amazed to see her full of life, running up and down the corridors with her drip trolley,' remembers Shelagh.

Throughout Lauren's treatment she had scans and checks and she went from strength to strength. Just before her second birthday, all the secondary tumours had gone and she had surgery to remove the tumour in the lung, by then down to a quarter of its original size. It was a dangerous four-hour operation because the tumour was so near to the spine and the heart. For Shelagh, now six months pregnant with her third daughter Fern, it was the longest morning of her life.

Amelia Lockwood, who also suffers from neuroblastoma, her father, and consultant Jon Pritchard – making treatment as fun as possible.

But yet again, Lauren defied expectations. Not only was the operation a complete success but she was able to come out of hospital after three days – instead of the expected two weeks – in time to celebrate her second birthday at home.

That might have been the end of treatment for Lauren but at that time doctors were trying to find out whether a new aggressive drug given at the end of treatment would further improve children's chances. They were running a randomised trial, meaning children, if parents agreed, were randomly allocated to have the treatment or not, and Lauren was one who was given the opportunity. 'We could have said no if we had wanted to,' says Shelagh, 'but I just felt that I was happier with her having it as it would kill any possible residual cells and I knew from her previous performance she would cope. She did.'

The drug was so aggressive that it would kill all of her bone marrow so, in preparation for one day's chemotherapy, Lauren had to have her own bone marrow harvested and then returned to her body 24 hours after the treatment. This was followed by three weeks confined to a sterile cubicle to allow her immunity to start to build back up. Then at last her treatment was over.

But the worry wasn't. 'We felt safer while she was receiving the drugs. But as soon as the drugs stop, that's when relapse can occur – and relapse is not easy to treat,' says Shelagh. The riskiest time was the next six months. Every month Lauren went back to Great Ormond Street for checks and there were many alarms. One scan showed a dark area on the shin bone which was thought possibly to be the start of another tumour but turned out to be a bruise from where Lauren had fallen off a slide. An X-ray showed a shadow on the lung and then seemingly abnormal cells turned up in her bone marrow but each time eventually there was an innocent explanation. 'There were so many frights. It was a scary time,' says Shelagh.

There was also a new baby demanding attention in the family. Fern was born after Lauren had finished her treatment. 'At first, when I found I was pregnant, it was a bit of a shock,' says Shelagh. 'We thought it was the last thing we would want to be coping with. But in fact my having the baby gave Lauren something to look forward to – and all of the rest of us something else to concern us. Fern was a blessing in disguise.

'And Lauren just got better and better. Her hair all grew back and now we go to Great Ormond Street for checks just once a year. The cancer hasn't stunted her growth. She plays football for a ladies team and she has her music. Sometimes it is all too easy to forget what she has been through.'

Consultant oncologist, Dr Jon Pritchard, to whom Shelagh and Peter remain enormously grateful, often cites Lauren's case when he is lecturing around the world. Survival for neuroblastoma has improved over the years but even so still stands at just 25 per cent.

For Lauren it is all a bit unreal. 'I don't remember any of it, of course, and I don't feel special or anything. In fact it is quite weird going into hospital for yearly checks when you've never felt anything was wrong with you!'

A PUZZLING CASE

Because Great Ormond Street is asked to take children from all over the country whose symptoms puzzle everyone else, often very rare cases and conditions tend to concentrate here. It means that, having seen all sorts of other cases, the staff become skilled in detecting problems which would be regarded as unthinkable in other hospitals.

An uncommon case was that of a three-year-old, who was seriously ill, suffering from mysterious fits. At first, no one could find out what was wrong with her: neither the family's general practitioner nor the paediatric unit at the local hospital could detect any reason for the fits. Brain scans had revealed nothing, nor did the child show any sign of an illness which could account for her sudden deterioration in health. Yet there was no doubt that something was seriously wrong. Perhaps specialists at Great Ormond Street, well versed in the rare forms of disease, could diagnose some malaise that the other doctors had missed.

Then something very odd was detected in the child's blood. For some reason, it contained abnormally high levels of salt, certainly high enough to cause sickness, diarrhoea and possibly brain damage. The only question was: how on earth did so much salt get into this toddler's blood in the first place?

Her father couldn't offer any explanation. Nor could her mother, although she did say that the little girl loved salty foods such as crisps.

Alarm bells began to sound in the mind of the examining consultant. He knew there was only one thing that could account for the high levels found in that child's bloodstream: someone had deliberately injected the young girl with salt.

At first no one believed him but, concerned by the puzzling case, social workers asked the family's local social services to keep a surreptitious eye on the child. When they explained why, the reaction was instant and furious. How could Great Ormond Street suggest that something was wrong? What a monstrous slur on a good mother. The request was dismissed, and the child was left off the At Risk register. But all argument about what to do ended when the child was rushed into hospital once more. This time she was very nearly dead.

Again, the little girl was transferred to Great Ormond Street's intensive care unit where, after a long struggle, she was nursed back to health. She had suffered exactly the same symptoms as before: severe fits and sickness before lapsing into unconsciousness. And once again, tests showed a huge amount of salt in her bloodstream.

Over the next few days, the girl was watched closely, but her symptoms didn't return. The level of salt in her blood had returned to normal, and regaining her strength, she was soon well enough to go on walks to the park with her mother. That's where she was when she had her next fit. Her mother dashed back on to the ward, and described to doctors in precise detail exactly what had happened. From what she said, it was clear that the little girl had certainly suffered another fit as the symptoms described were classic. And yet, when the girl was examined and more tests performed, there was still no sign of a fit ever having occurred. Again, the girl was watched carefully on the ward, without result. However, after a few days, on yet another visit to the park with her mother, the same thing happened again.

That's when a peculiar coincidence became very obvious. For some strange reason, despite being in a hospital crammed with highly sophisticated medical equipment and staffed by teams of highly experienced doctors and nurses, this little girl's fits were only ever witnessed by one person – her mother. It was time for a lengthy discussion.

At first she denied being in any way to blame, but when confronted with the findings, she eventually confessed to deliberately passing a tube into the little girl's rectum and injecting her with strong solutions of salt. Trusting her mum, the child had been too young to associate what she was doing with her subsequent illnesses and fits. Her older child too had been subjected to this treatment until he became old enough to be able to speak well, increasing the danger of him revealing what was going on.

Without further delay, both children were taken into care.

While such a case is alarming enough, tragically, some children admitted to Great Ormond Street have been victims of even more obvious and brutal treatment. As one of the largest children's hospitals in the south east of England, it sees its fair share of babies and toddlers who have been deliberately beaten and abused by adults. Sometimes, the injuries have been caused in a rare moment of uncontrolled anger. Sometimes, the attacker has simply enjoyed inflicting the pain.

And if that was not enough, physical abuse is not the only form of torment some young patients will have known. Others may have been sexually abused, often for years, by members of their own family. Others may have fallen victim to child pornographers and paedophile rings. Becoming a target for paedophiles is a danger every children's hospital must bear in mind, and at Great Ormond Street even the volunteers are subject to extremely close scrutiny.

Thankfully, such cases of deliberate abuse are comparatively rare but, sadly, do find their way to Great Ormond Street from time to time.

FAMILY-CENTRED CARE

At Great Ormond Street, as the hospital's motto so clearly states, the children come 'first and always'. However, the youth and vulnerability of the patients mean that their parents and families are closely involved in every part of their treatment.

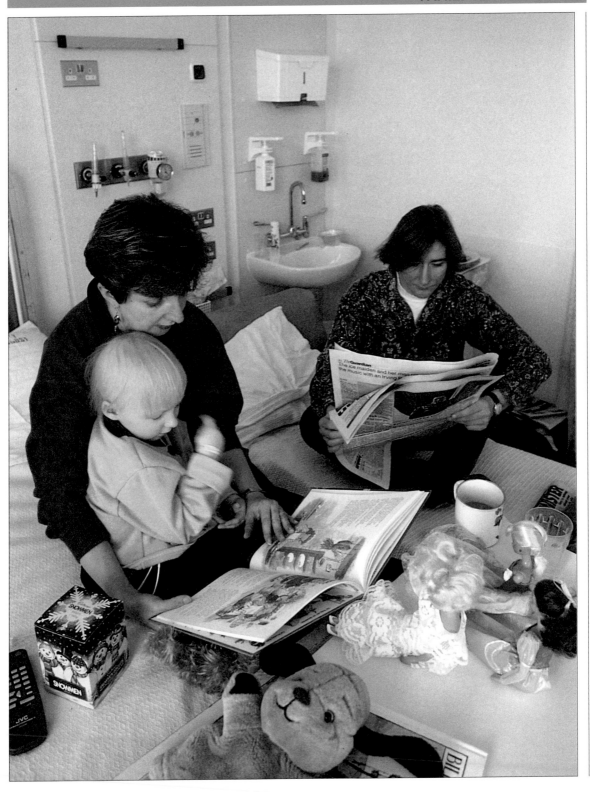

Despite the constant care and attention children receive in hospital, there is no doubt that they need their parents with them. In fact, it has been shown that sick children get better more quickly when their parents are nearby: they are happier, feel safer and are generally much more secure.

Of course, the staff at Great Ormond Street are more than mindful of the pressures parents face in the process, and do their best to provide every type of support possible, from counselling and practical help with financial problems to aromatherapy massages provided by a dedicated volunteer. Even so, many parents must cope under extraordinary circumstances, and put up with the most devastating experiences imaginable. A huge number willingly submerge their own lives and risk financial ruin to bring any comfort possible to their child.

COUNSELLING AND SUPPORT

One of the staff who deals extensively with parents is former social worker, now Bereavement Services Co-ordinator, Jean Simons.

'I find the courage displayed by the people I meet at this hospital extremely humbling. I wonder where they find this inner strength that helps them cope. I feel, like many of the staff here, that I couldn't cope myself with many of the things that some of the parents have to. But when it comes to the crunch ordinary people can become extraordinarily strong on behalf of their child.

'I have known people who have had to watch their child become disfigured by illness, knowing that their ultimate death is inevitable. In the midst of it all, these parents can still find the strength to worry about what video their child would like to watch and go to extraordinary lengths to plan a treat, even one as simple as a trip to the park.

'But there are some things I can't help them with,' says Jean, and for most of the major issues, parents have no option but to work through their feelings themselves. What someone like a social worker can do, however, is give the parents a chance to talk.

'That person is often seen as a neutral party by parents,' she says, 'someone who isn't part of the medical or nursing staff, yet who, nevertheless, understands the traumatic experience that having a seriously ill child places upon people. Parents will often say things that they won't even confess to their own

'If you take away a sick child from its parent . . . you break its heart immediately'

DR GEORGE ARMSTRONG,
FOUNDER OF 'THE DISPENSARY FOR THE INFANT POOR', OPENED IN LONDON IN 1769

partners, because they know that probably the social workers will have heard other people say the same thing before. They will talk about things that are going wrong in their relationships, how they can't devote sufficient time to a partner, to their other children, or to themselves. They may feel helpless and guilty.

'They lose confidence in their own abilities as a parent because they cannot ensure their child's survival. In different times, before illness struck, each had been used to the feeling of being able to take control of their child's life. They have become used to making decisions on their child's behalf, and being able to organise the future around their child's welfare.

'When the doctor says "Your child has cancer; we can treat him/her, but there is no guarantee," parents are crushed by the realisation that even if they have done everything right for their child, there is no way they can be certain that the child will live.'

> *'...parents are crushed by the realisation that, even if they have done everything right for their child, there is no way they can be certain that their child will live.'*
>
> JEAN SIMONS
> BEREAVEMENT SERVICES
> CO-ORDINATOR

FINANCIAL PROBLEMS

The financial strain can be enormous. Research shows that within six months of their child being diagnosed with a serious illness, such as cancer, families may lose up to 50 per cent of their income. At first, a parent may take unpaid leave to be with the child, going back to work after a few weeks, only to take more unpaid leave as the child goes to outpatients for treatment. One parent – often the mother – may have a part-time job, and if she gives this up it is a sudden wallop to the family's finances, forcing them to operate on a lot less income at a time when their expenditure is spiralling.

Travelling to and from Great Ormond Street can cost a lot of money, and taxis, which they wouldn't normally take, are often the only means of getting a family and a sick child from a train station to the hospital. Even though food in the hospital is subsidised, it's still an extra expense. And even when the family is at home again at the end of a long day, it may be necessary to rely on expensive convenience foods. Within a few weeks following diagnosis at a hospital like Great Ormond Street, a family's budget can be in tatters.

For people who are self-employed, there is no such thing as paid leave and the difficulties are immediately apparent. If they take time off work, they don't get paid and the more time they spend with their child in hospital, the less time they are putting into finding new work, and soon the business may be in trouble. A very real fear for many parents is repossession of their home, particularly for families who are self-employed.

Parents who are living on state benefits, ironically, don't see such a drastic change in their income. Many of the extra expenses will make them eligible for additional payments which will cover at least some of the burden. However, they too are not immune from hardship. Every parent, knowing that their child is desperately sick and may die, wants to buy them little treats and take them on holiday, perhaps for the last time. Imagine what that must be like for a mother who knows that the

Kate Birch, who is 12, suffers from Hodgkin's disease and attends GOS as a day patient. Her parents are there to support her whenever she is undergoing treatment.

benefits she receives from the state will not stretch anywhere near that far. Money worries are the last thing she needs.

When parents first come to this hospital they may say, in response to offers of help, 'Money doesn't matter. All I want to think about is my child getting well.' But unfortunately, three months down the line, it is often a different story.

COMPANY AND ISOLATION

In contrast to such difficulties, Sue Whymark found her stay at Great Ormond Street – for the treatment of her son, Joshua – almost wonderful.

A single parent, Sue had spent a year in isolation, alone at home with three-year-old Joshua. This was due to his extremely rare immune disorder, called PNP, which had left him defenceless against all kinds of infections, so she had been advised to avoid contact with other people as much as possible. Sue and Joshua stayed in the hospital for 10 weeks while he had a bone-marrow transplant to save his life. (For more about Joshua and Sue, see Chapter 5.)

'As a divorced mother, forced to keep away from as many people as possible for Joshua's sake, I had been very isolated and lonely. In hospital I had so many people around me. For me it was really good. The nurses were so easy to talk to about anything, not just Joshua. Before they got busy with the medicines in the evening, often they would make a point of coming in to me with a coffee for a chat, because they knew I was on my own.

'They were so intuitive. If I got very low, they often realised before I did, said they would take care of Joshua and sent me window-shopping in the West End. I often hadn't appreciated how low I had become until I went out, and came back feeling it had done me a world of good. Going out for a walk round the streets near the hospital just isn't the same, because there isn't much of interest round the hospital to walk to. You just feel you are tramping the same old boring streets.

Despite having to live at the hospital for weeks on end, Sue Whymark enjoyed the company of other people, especially the nursing staff.

'My five-year-old daughter, Vicky, was being cared for by my parents. The hospital offered one of their houses outside the hospital so that Vicky could come up and stay any time, with her grandma, if she wanted to see us. In fact, we didn't do that often because she got bored and was happier away from the hospital.

'I really missed the company when finally we left hospital because we

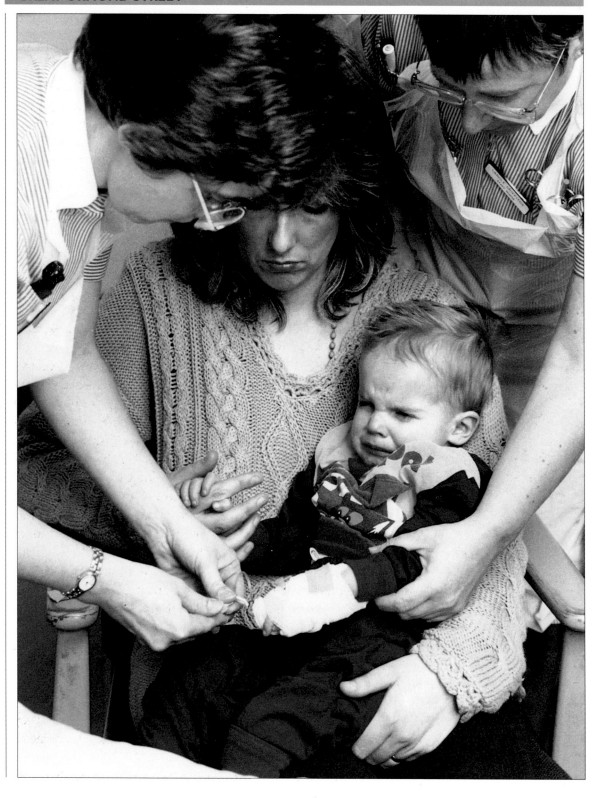

had to return to remaining isolated at home again for a while. I thought I would ring up a lot just for a chat with the nurses – they like that because it is good for their morale to have contact with a child who gets better – but there was so much I had to do at home that I just didn't have enough time to call them much. I do think about them a lot though. They are very special people.'

'BEING THERE'

Most parents will do everything they can to save their child's life, and the most frustrating thing for them is a feeling of sheer helplessness. Often they will stay by the child's bedside day and night, until they are exhausted, afraid to leave in case something happens in their absence. It's as if their very presence were a talisman to ward off evil.

Some parents on the point of exhaustion will, nevertheless, insist on being with their child no matter what procedure is being carried out. One such case stands out particularly.

The hospital had admitted a three-year-old girl, born with defective kidneys, who had not reacted well to her first kidney transplant. From the earliest days of her birth, her parents had moulded their lives around hers, caring for every aspect of her health. The kidney dialysis she needed regularly was done at home. They were devoted to her, and despite the burden of her ill health, the child was central to their lives. The transplant, which had promised so much, had not gone well, and she had contracted a bacterial infection. It spread rapidly through her body, and when she came into the hospital's intensive care unit, she was already very ill. Soon, she developed lung problems, and with her heart under so much stress, her prospects were very bleak indeed.

For all of those three short years of her life, her parents had done everything they could for her, and so they weren't prepared to step back now. Although they knew the staff would their utmost, they didn't want to hand their child over to strangers entirely, and insisted on staying by her bedside as the doctors tried to save her life. Knowing the anguish most parents feel even at the sight of their child in tears, this was obviously going to be a very hard time for them. However, from earlier conversations with staff, there was no doubt that they were prepared for everything. They wanted their child to know that she was not alone. They were with her every step of the way, no matter how unpleasant some of the medical procedures would be.

'The cardiac arrest, when it came, was hardly a total surprise, but swift

A mother's familiar cuddle is reassuring for patients who are too young to understand what is happening to them.

and sudden nevertheless,' says the doctor. 'As soon as the alarm on the monitor sounded, the intensive care team went into a well-rehearsed resuscitation procedure. While one of us pumped the young girl's chest, another team member drew up drugs to stimulate the heart, before we resorted to using an electric shock. But still the parents wanted to be there. In the midst of all the flurry of activity, they kept talking to their child saying; "Come on, you can do it. You can pull through." But there was nothing we could do.

'After she died, I knew that both her mother and father would want to be left alone with their child, and so all the equipment which surrounded the bed was taken away, and for the first time since coming onto the intensive care unit, the little girl again looked like the child they had known and loved.

'That's when they decided to take her home themselves. They couldn't bear the thought of leaving her alone in a cold hospital mortuary. They had not deserted her before, and so they were not going to desert her now. I knew it was the right thing for this particular family. They would never have felt comfortable leaving her here, and I understood exactly how they must be feeling.

'It wasn't the first time that this request had been made by some parents, and I knew what arrangements had to be made. The couple were in no condition to drive themselves, and it is the hospital's policy that an escort is always provided in these circumstances. In their state, the risk of crashing their car would have been too great. It had to be someone else who was not emotionally involved, and who could handle the situation with care and sensitivity.'

The difficult task of driving the car fell to one of Great Ormond Street's myriad volunteers. The driver was given a letter confirming that the child had died in Great Ormond Street Hospital, lest anything should happen during the journey prompting questions about the body.

And that is how they took their daughter home: in her mother's arms, wrapped in a warm hospital blanket, on the back seat of a volunteer's car and accompanied by a nurse all the way from London.

A MOTHER'S DILEMMA

Not all parents can stand the ordeal of watching their children being treated during an emergency, and for many, even the sight of an injection being given is almost too much to bear. A few find the stress so great that they prefer not to be at Great Ormond Street at all.

There was a new-born boy, suffering from a very serious inherited lung condition, who had come in from another hospital's maternity unit. Normally, in these instances, the mother naturally wants to visit the child as soon as possible, but this case was different. Days passed, and even though the baby was very seriously ill, his mother never came to the hospital to see him.

A member of staff rang the mother every day to report on the child's condition but, each time, she said it was too difficult to come to the hospital. At first, she said she couldn't afford her train fare, but that excuse was easily overcome by the ward social worker offering to pay for the ticket. Then she said she couldn't afford accommodation in London, but a solution was offered for that, too. Then she said that her husband was too busy at work to take time off, and so she had to stay at home to look after her other two children.

Three weeks had passed and, during that time, her child's condition was steadily deteriorating. There was little that could be done, and it was only a matter of time before the little boy would die. And still neither his mother nor his father had come to see him.

Finally, it was decided that since the baby was going to die, he should be returned to the parents' local hospital, so that at least their baby would be close by in his final days. But when the mother was told, she objected, and at last, agreed to visit the child at Great Ormond Street.

That's when the true story emerged. It turned out that this little boy was her eighth pregnancy. Two children had survived, but there had been four other miscarriages, and her first child had died shortly after birth – from exactly the same disease which had brought this little boy to Great Ormond Street. Far from being an uncaring mother, the news that this baby too was suffering from the same disease which had claimed the life of her first child had come as a tremendous blow. That death had cost her years of agony, and now the thought that she would have to go through the whole painful process again with her new-born son was too much to contemplate. So she had made a deliberate decision not to see the child. She knew that if she did, she would be bonded as a mother, and that would make the baby's death every bit as unbearable and agonising as before.

Only then did it become apparent why the mother had gone to such lengths to avoid coming to the hospital. Deliberately denying her maternal bonds must have been a very difficult decision to make, and it gave an indication of just how great the pain caused by the death of her first child must have been.

She stayed by that baby's side for the few days that remained, cuddling her dying son as any other mother would have done. In the end, she was glad she had come, because it allowed her to get to know the baby boy although it was only for a very short time.

THE PAIN OF SEPARATION

Not all the problems that are faced by children and their families are entirely medical. There are also children – for example, some in intensive care – whose prime cause of suffering is simple bureaucracy. They have recovered from their illness, they are ready to leave the unit, but very occasionally the hospitals which asked Great Ormond Street to care for them in the first instance refuse to take them back.

Although such children are still dependent upon a ventilator for every breath, they are in a stable condition, and have been for some time. There is no reason why these children should not go back to their local hospitals where they would be closer to home, and to their parents and families. Instead, they are denied the fundamental right of every child to be near the warmth and love of its parents.

Each hospital provides a range of excuses, such as they don't have the

Nursing staff keep a special eye on any children whose parents have to be absent for any length of time.

right facilities, or they don't have the right staff to care for them properly. What they don't mention is another factor which undoubtedly plays a major role in keeping these children away from their families. Taking them back would also cost the hospitals a lot of money.

Looking after a child on a ventilator is expensive. They require constant vigilance, and occupy an expensive hospital bed for the foreseeable future. Now that many hospitals are controlled by trusts, under pressure to keep within tight monetary budgets, there must be a great temptation to delay accepting an expensive patient for as long as possible.

For example, one boy, jumping from the top bunk of his bed as young boys will, fell awkwardly and hit his head. It was a simple accident but one that almost cost him his life. As blood seeped into his brain, the trauma team who treated him at his local hospital did the best they could, but it wasn't enough to halt the damage being caused to his lungs, and so he was eventually sent to Great Ormond Street.

Now, he has recovered from the head injury, and with time and physiotherapy, may eventually improve sufficiently to come off the ventilator. But still his hospital won't take him back, four months after the accident. His mother lives almost 300 miles away and has two other children. For her, coming to London every day is impossible, but she makes the arduous return trip every weekend to see her child. Her son is now terribly homesick and cries much of the time, especially when he sees other parents visiting their children in the unit.

Transferring the child to a local hospital would be the obvious solution, but even though all the hospitals close to home have been approached, no one will take him. In the meantime, the boy is separated from his mother for no good reason.

Stephanie Collard and her mother came to the hospital for removal of a tumour on her spine.

WORKING TO KEEP FAMILIES TOGETHER

One of the invaluable facilities at Great Ormond Street is the accommodation provided for parents in or near the hospital. Beds are available in all the wards – from temporary Z-beds put up when needed in a ward playroom to convertible couches in the more modern rooms. The Wishing Well Appeal, which ran from 1987 to 1989, contributed funds to buy the Italian Hospital nearby, which has been converted into rooms for parents plus four self-contained flats where children recovering from transplant surgery who are well enough to leave hospital, but still need treatment, can stay with their families. As well, the Sick Children's Trust, a separate charity, has accommodation nearby that can be used by families of patients in a number of different London hospitals, including Great Ormond Street.

Someone who became grateful for this sort of facility was a mother whose two-year-old daughter, Simone, was suffering from a rare form of leukaemia. Her treatment was to involve a prolonged course of chemotherapy which extended her stay at the hospital into months.

The mother had been a successful career woman with a large, comfortable house, an expensive company car and a nanny. Suddenly, every aspect of her life seemed to have changed almost overnight – including her marriage. Just before Simone's illness was diagnosed, she had told her husband she wanted a divorce.

But her problems were not confined to Simone's illness.

'While time ticked slowly past inside the hospital, outside the world could not and would not stand still. I had other responsibilities to take care of, and none more important than Vanessa, my eldest daughter who at four years old was having to cope first with her father leaving home, and then Simone and me spending all of our time in hospital.

'At first, she was cared for by a nanny, but as time progressed, she moved in with my brother and his family in London. However, I was very concerned by how little time I was devoting to Vanessa, and eventually she came to live with me in a house owned by a charitable trust, just five minutes' walk away from Simone's ward. It was like a home from home, enabling me at last to begin to pick up at least some of the familiar strands of my life.

'A typical day would begin at 7am when I woke up Vanessa and got her dressed. Then both of us would go to the hospital to have breakfast with Simone on the ward. When we had finished, I would leave Simone playing by her bed, and take Vanessa to a nearby nursery school which had kindly agreed to accept her. Then it was back to the hospital to give Simone my undivided attention for about two hours, as well as comfort her during any treatment. At midday, I would collect Vanessa from the nursery and bring her to the hospital again, so that she could have lunch with Simone and play with her on the bed.

'By that time, Simone would be feeling tired, so whenever I had the chance, I would leave her to sleep and take Vanessa shopping or to the park, so that she too felt she had a mother who loved her and took time

to be with her. Then it was back to the hospital for tea with Simone before leaving her at 6.30 to take Vanessa home to our temporary accommodation. I would talk to her about what she had done during the day, read her stories before putting her to bed, and attempt to give her the love and warmth she deserved.

The hospital radio station is another source of amusement and distraction – for both children and parents.

'It was a juggling act that worked well as long as Simone had a good night, but sometimes she was desperately ill, and I needed to be there to look after her. Once, we thought she was beginning to have heart failure brought on by the severity of her treatment, and at times like these, I would have no option but to keep Vanessa with me on the ward, sometimes up to 11 at night. It wasn't an ideal existence, but Vanessa was so happy at being together as a family again that this overcame all the disadvantages.

'My divorce was under way as well. For the previous two and a half years I had known that my marriage wasn't right, and the last six months had been sheer misery. My husband, finding it difficult to cope emotionally with Simone's illness, tended to stay away from the hospital. When he did come, I found his visits fraught with tension and occasional bad temper. He too was under stress, and sometimes shouted at hospital staff if he thought things weren't being done properly.

'While I understood the reason for his frustrations, his behaviour did, nevertheless, make life difficult for me, and it came as no surprise that our divorce was bitterly fought, often involving hour-long conversations to solicitors from the ward's public telephone. Maybe I would have been better off postponing our divorce until after Simone's illness, but I could see no point in prolonging the issue because I knew I never wanted to live with him again.

'In a strange way, the battle over our divorce kept me sane. It was an element of the outside world which I could not ignore, occasionally demanding my attention, and diverting my gaze from the sight of my sick child lying in the cot beside me.

'Problems with marriages were very common among all of the parents on the ward, no matter how stable their relationship had been beforehand. I wasn't surprised. Many of the mothers beside me had two or three other children at home, and suddenly the responsibility for every aspect of their care had fallen heavily upon their husbands. In addition, the men had to go to work to provide the family with money. No one was there to pay them any attention, and I'm sure many of them missed their sex lives. For month after month, they had to contend with this pressured existence, as well as worry about their sick child in hospital. Nor was I surprised when the stress sometimes boiled over on the ward with blazing arguments between husband and wife.

'All of the mothers on that ward had formed close bonds with each other. When one child suffered, we all felt the pain. They were like my own family, and occasionally we would all be in tears when one of our children was at a low. It didn't matter who you were or where you came from. Simply being the mother of a sick child was enough to cut across all social classes and different backgrounds because we knew we would each have to face the same hurdles in the days ahead.'

ASK MRS BERRY!

Another mother who has virtually lived at the hospital is Alison Berry. In fact, after a stay with her son Jamie that lasted the best part of two years, she was so familiar with the hospital that even doctors would ask her the quickest route from one part of it to another.

Five-year-old Jamie's complicated gut disorder meant a number of tests, operations and trial treatments. 'I slept in his bed with him often enough or else in a room for mothers, in bunks four to a room,' says Alison. 'I really didn't mind living in the hospital. I didn't yearn to be at home and I wasn't bothered by a hospital atmosphere.' (For more about Jamie, see Chapter 9.)

At one stage, Jamie was so seriously ill he had to be nursed in intensive care and David, his father, decided to give up his job and come to live in the hospital too. 'We were then put in the Italian wing, flats and suites that are outside Great Ormond Street. When this wing first opened, it was pure luxury to me. It was lovely to have a room with your own shower.

'Then we went into Rainbow House, one of the houses run by the Sick Children's Trust. It was bliss to have a kitchen. But before we had that, I didn't often leave Jamie and even when I did, I sometimes got called back because he had woken and was upset without me.

'I think the worst part about hospital living was the lack of cooking facilities and the fact that there was only one washing machine which was often broken. You'd traipse to the other side of the hospital with your washing and find it was being used. Or else someone else had left a sock in it and your washing turned pink. My washing machine was the one thing from home I truly missed!

'I didn't feel isolated or bored in the hospital. Because Jamie wasn't actually ill most of the time, we could take him out a lot all over the place. And the nurses on the ward were wonderful. Often I sat up chatting with them till 11. They became my friends but, because we were there so long, many came and went and that was quite sad. Doctors too. We went to a lot of leaving parties.

'In a way we now miss the hospital because, when you are there for so long, you lose contact with friends at home and when you are home, you then lose contact with the nurses. We've found it quite lonely at times.

'There were always new patients and new parents to get to know. We would listen to their troubles, help them get settled in, tell them how to get around the hospital. Everyone new was always referred to Mrs Berry!'

4 INTENSIVE CARE

The intensive care unit at Great Ormond Street treats the most acutely ill children. Some are new-born babies, brought straight to the unit from hospitals all over Britain. Others are older children, struck down by illness or recovering from major surgery, who need a level of care which can only be provided by at least one and sometimes two nurses constantly by their bedside. Many are so ill that they cannot breathe for themselves, relying instead upon a mechanical ventilator to take their every breath. Often the machinery that surrounds the bed is much bigger than the child itself.

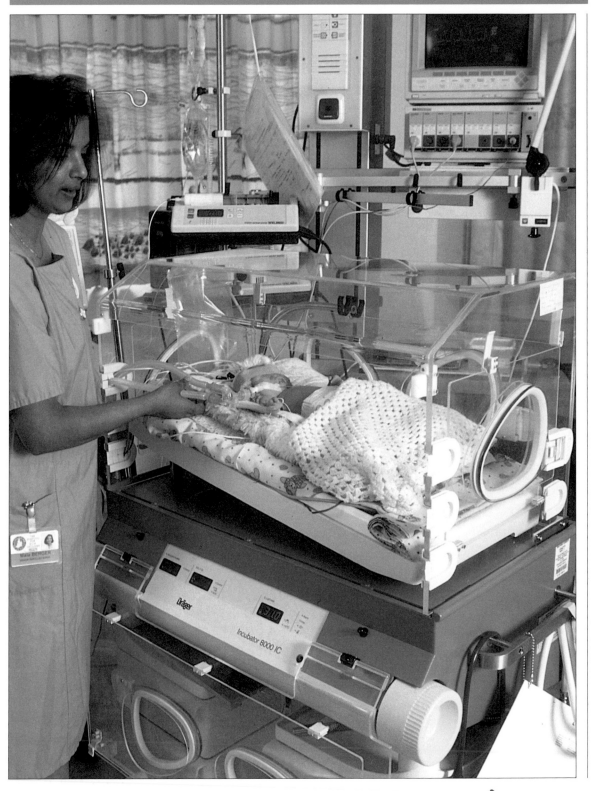

Sometimes the sound of an emergency alarm fills the unit, warning staff that a ventilator, blowing air into the lungs of a sick child, is no longer working. In such cases time is critical, and doctors run to the scene, going through in their minds the procedures that are needed to save the child's life.

However, on one occasion, everyone soon burst out laughing, and the reason became immediately apparent.

'Four-year-old Alex had deliberately pulled the plug on his ventilator again,' says Consultant Intensivist, Dr Quen Mok. 'He was cross because he thought the little girl in the next bed was getting too much attention, so he disconnected the tubes, setting off the alarm and forcing the nurses to run to him. It's a simple ploy, but it works every time, because we can never take the risk of assuming that he is just messing around again.'

Seeing children continue to act like children, despite being surrounded by the daunting technology of an intensive care unit is one of the reasons why Dr Mok chose to be a paediatrician.

'Children are remarkably resilient,' she says.'They tend to become ill extremely quickly, but at the same time, they have the ability to recover from injuries that would probably kill an adult. And as soon as children begin to feel better, they will certainly let you know. You just can't keep them in bed, because they want to be up doing things. They want to run around and play even though they were seriously ill just a few days earlier. It's that joy for life that I find most rewarding.

'Many of the sick children I see aren't old enough to tell me what is wrong with them. Instead, I rely upon a special form of communication which has developed with experience, and I know the signs to watch out for. Critics often say that treating very young children is more akin to veterinary medicine than anything else, but I disagree. Handing a healthy child back to its parents when everyone thought it was going to die gives me a special feeling that I haven't found in any other branch of medicine. And anyway, vets get paid a lot more than I do.'

Dr Mok is one of four consultants who specialise in intensive care. The two wards that make up the intensive care department – neonatal (Dolphin) and paediatric (Seahorse) – are equipped to look after 29 children, but at the moment no more than 16 are accepted at one time. It's not a shortage of money that keeps almost half of the beds empty in this badly needed unit, but a desperate lack of properly trained inten-

'Handing a healthy child back to its parents when everyone thought it was going to die gives me a special feeling'

D R Q U E N M O K

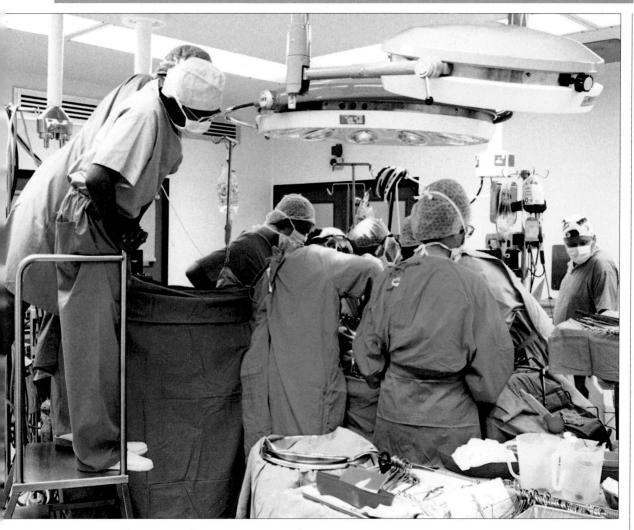

In surgery, it is not unusual for trainees or nurses to watch the procedure from a distance, standing out of the way on a raised platform.

sive care nurses. It is very stressful and demanding work, and there is also the extra expense of working in central London on National Health Service wages. As a result, almost 50 per cent of children who need intensive care at Great Ormond Street have to be turned away. Even so, approximately 200 newly born babies and almost 500 older children are treated every year.

FIGHTING FOR LIFE

The intensive care unit receives many serious cases that other hospitals are not able to treat. One of these was a little girl who had contracted a very serious bacterial infection which was now poisoning her blood. She had been rushed to her local hospital, but realising just how ill she was, the doctors had immediately asked Great Ormond Street to admit her.

The intensive care department has an emergency retrieval unit. A medical team can be sent in a specially equipped ambulance to examine, and if necessary bring back to Great Ormond Street, children in any part of the country who have a life-threatening illness. At once, the emergency team was dispatched to stabilise the girl's condition and supervise her trip back to the hospital. When she arrived, her blood pressure was already very low, her heart beat was failing, and she couldn't breathe for herself. She was going downhill very quickly and her prospects were not good.

She was given drugs to improve her heart, but steadily, her condition deteriorated still further. She was unconscious, and her flesh had become puffy and bloated. Gradually, as the infection got worse, other vital organs went into decline. Over the next week, her kidneys failed, then her heart became worse, needing an increasing amount of drugs to maintain the correct beat and rhythm. Numerous drugs and machinery were being used to take over the function of other vital organs and keep her alive.

'Reluctantly, I began to believe that she wasn't going to make it,' says Dr Mok. Her body was beginning to fight its own tissue: a well-known reaction to severe infection which in itself often proves fatal.

Laurie Didham is one of about 30 volunteers who staff the Child Death Helpline. All the volunteers have lost a child themselves, and offer support to other parents, all over the country, who are going through the same trauma.

'Yet I knew that this was a reversible condition. I was treating the infection with antibiotics, and if I could only keep the little girl alive for a few days more, then I knew she might turn the corner.

'I warned her parents that she might not recover, but they were determined to try everything. They were very upset but asked us to continue to do all that we could.

'I couldn't give them much hope because there was little to give. And to make matters worse, patches of the little girl's tissue were now turning gangrenous as the bacterial infection spread. Again, I warned her parents that, even if she were to recover, she could lose her toes or fingers. The little girl's prospects were looking very bleak.'

Her heart was the first thing to recover. Slowly, the strength of the beat improved, and then her kidneys picked up, until she had reached such a good level of recovery that the doctors were able to begin weaning her off a long list of drugs.

'I was ecstatic. She had been receiving so many different treatments that I couldn't say for certain which one had been the turning point. Whatever it was, I felt elated that the work done by everyone on that intensive care team had been rewarded by this young life. Quite a few times, I thought we would lose her, but each day she managed to survive a little longer. And now, here she was, well on the road to recovery.'

A frustrating aspect of working in intensive care is that as soon as the children no longer need intensive treatment, they are transferred to another ward. This policy keeps beds free for other acute cases, but it does mean that few staff on the unit get to see children when they have fully recovered. Since most of the children are sedated during their stay, mercifully few of them remember anything about their ordeal and the procedures they had to undergo to make them well again. But as a result, few return to let the staff see just how well they have become.

'But this little girl didn't forget us. She walked onto the ward: healthy, bright and full of energy. It was wonderful to see her looking so well, because we all knew how close to death she had been. Sadly, the gangrene had taken its toll, forcing surgeons to amputate her right leg below the knee. Nevertheless she was alive, and there had been times when I thought I would never see this day.'

NEONATAL CARE

Baby Michael Bond was also treated at the intensive care unit. When only five weeks old he suddenly went blue and started breathing very

It's hard to imagine that this handsome chap was once so ill he had to be rushed into intensive care.

fast, and was swiftly taken by ambulance to his local hospital in Hemel Hempstead. There, doctors suspected bronchiolitis, a respiratory disorder usually caused by a virus. However, as the local hospital lacked the facilities to run the necessary tests and care for Michael fully, the intensive care emergency retrieval unit was called in.

Michael was lucky. Because of immense pressure on the available beds, almost as many children as are admitted have to be treated elsewhere.

In this case, the intensive care team brought with them an incubator, and made the decision to have a ventilator do the breathing for him: this means a tube is inserted into the airway and connected to the ventilator, which takes over the breathing and blows a mixture of oxygen and air in and out of the lungs.

On arrival at intensive care, Michael was taken to a cubicle and hooked up to the highly sophisticated equipment there. The equipment in one of the unit's cubicles costs about £87,000. It costs another £218,000 a year to keep each cubicle running and to staff it but the expense is more than justified each time a child's life is saved.

Unable to travel in the intensive care unit's ambulance, Michael's parents arrived at the unit an hour later and, like many parents, were initially overwhelmed to see all the technology and machinery in use to treat their child.

Michael's breathing needed to be stabilised but he didn't need drugs or any other treatment. The laboratory was unable to identify a viral cause of his illness but his full recovery was quick, and 48 hours after his admittance he was able to go home.

DIFFICULTIES WITH DIAGNOSIS

Despite the huge range of expertise and equipment at Great Ormond Street, a clear diagnosis is not always possible.

A six-year-old unconscious girl was brought in by the retrieval team from Newham General Hospital. She had felt sick, started twitching and then 'drifted off', her mother says. In the ambulance, on the way to the hospital, the team had noted that her jaw seemed to be locked and they suspected a fit. She was sedated in case she had suffered some kind of bleeding in the brain.

Once in intensive care, she received a scan to check whether there was any raised brain pressure, but the scan was normal. Next came a lumbar puncture, to take a sample of spinal fluid to check for infections, such as meningitis. This test was also clear. About 12 hours after her fit, the little girl woke and the breathing tubes could be removed from her nose.

As she seemed well, she was able to leave the next day, although it had not been possible to diagnose the cause of her fit. Another fit a few months later, however, confirmed she had epilepsy.

THE STRESSES OF THE JOB

As well as treating the acutely ill children who come into intensive care, the staff also interact closely with the parents. Even so, it is not always plain sailing. The parents of children admitted to intensive care are often in an extremely stressful position, not knowing whether their child is going to live or die, and having to rely upon strangers for the answer. Under such stress, it's no wonder that parents often get very angry and try to find someone to blame for their children's illness. Says Dr Mok: 'Usually, that turns out to be their general practitioner, their local hospital, and often, all of the staff on this unit including me. I remember one woman who said quite bluntly: "I hate you. Every time you speak to me, you give me bad news." I could see her point, but at the same time, I was doing all that I could to save the life of her child.

'There are times in this job when I go home at the end of the day and I don't want to talk to anyone. There are also times when I feel so tired that I just want to go to bed, to be woken up for dinner, and then go back to bed again.

'The hardest thing I have to do is to tell parents that there is nothing more we can do for their child. Their child is going to die, or if it does survive, it will be severely handicapped.

'I used to think that this part of the job would become easier with time and experience, but I was wrong. Instead, it becomes harder and harder. There is no formula that can be applied to every case, and nor should there be one. To every parent, each child is special, and so it is only fair that they should be able to command a special part of my attention. There are still some parents that I cry with, no matter how hard I try to stop myself. It's quite embarrassing at times, but I don't think that anyone really minds. They realise that I have been doing my best to help their child, and it is only natural that I too should be affected by what has happened.

'I find it difficult to walk away from the unit at the end of a day and

Like all the other wards, the intensive care unit has its own reception area and nurses' station. The staff are always aware of the stresses faced by anxious parents and do their best to create a reassuring atmosphere.

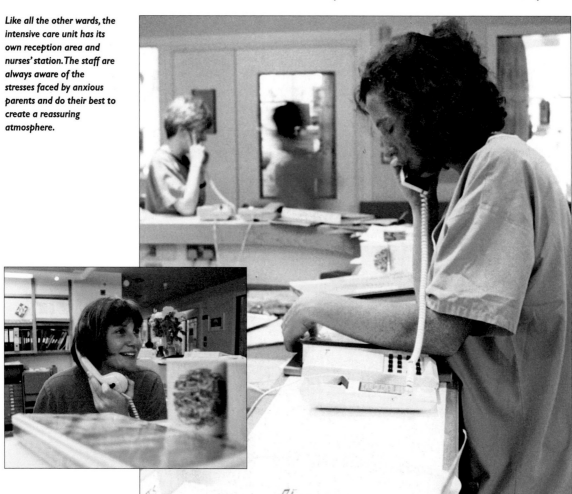

simply forget all about the children here until the following morning. Often, there are cases that I worry about when I go home. It's usually the children who are very ill and unstable, the cases where I'm not sure what is wrong with the child, or a problem that I haven't yet worked out.

'In the evening, I'll read up on a condition to make sure there is nothing I have missed, nothing else I should have done. I'll sometimes ring the unit before I go to bed, to make sure everything is all right, and if a child is in a very poor condition then I won't go home at all.

'Some will say that this is bad practice, that I should be able to switch off completely for my patients' benefit as well as my own. But I disagree. So much of my life is tied up in my work, and I wouldn't have it any other way.'

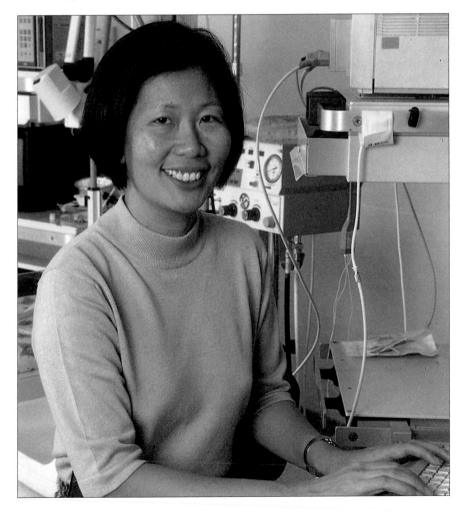

Dr Quen Mok, one of Great Ormond Street's four Consultant Intensivists, finds it difficult to stop thinking about her job when she is away from the hospital.

5 INFECTIOUS DISEASES AND IMMUNOLOGY

The units at Great Ormond Street that deal with infectious diseases and immunology (problems with resistance to disease) are combined into what's called the Host Defence Directorate. This means that two very specialised areas can work closely together in a unique way.

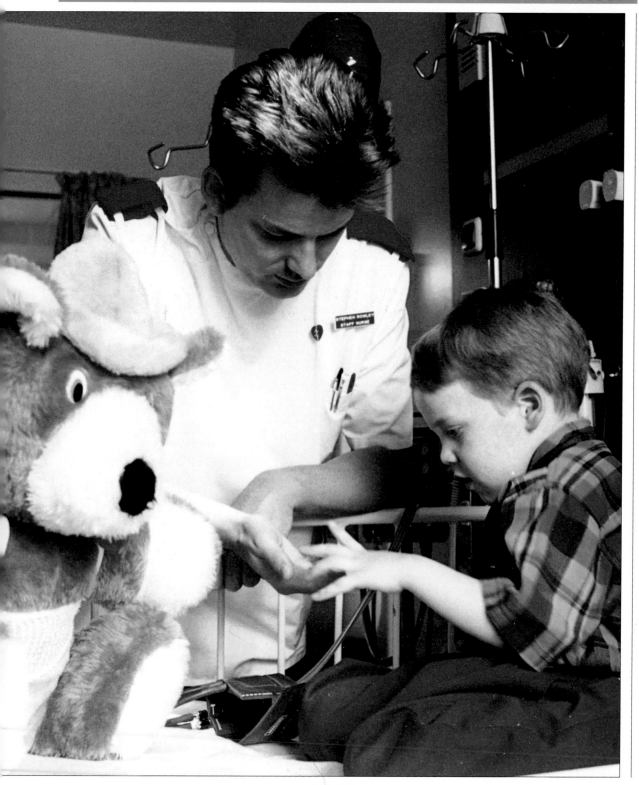

Dr Vas Novelli, consultant to the infectious diseases unit, is justifiably proud of the work carried out in his field at Great Ormond Street, and feels that the unit is able to offer a superior service, not just because of the link with immunology, but also thanks to the wide range of specialist care available within the hospital complex.

'Because this is a tertiary referral hospital, we only see the most rare, severe and complicated diseases that local hospitals are not able to deal with,' he says. 'Typically, these may include tropical diseases, such as cerebral malaria, perhaps picked up when families have gone abroad on holiday; unusual forms of meningitis; tuberculosis; hepatitis; and infections that are difficult to identify, known as pyrexia [fevers] of unknown origin. Sometimes a child might be treated by up to five or six different consultants working together.'

As well as these diseases, sadly a major part of his work concerns children who are infected with HIV, or who have developed Aids, or Aids-related conditions. Again, the service offered is all-encompassing, with outpatient clinics as well as inpatient care. At present, the hospital cares for about 150 families who have a member or members infected with the virus, and can offer them multi-disciplinary facilities, including intensive care support if required.

Dr Novelli is a specialist in infectious diseases, but liaises closely with colleagues in immunology.

An important part of this work involves medical trials. 'We are still trying to work out the best way to treat these children,' says Dr Novelli.

The immunology unit is concerned with children who have congenital deficiencies in their immune system (that is, those present from birth), and part of their work includes the pioneering technique of bone marrow transplants. Marrow is the soft core of bone, and is a highly active tissue in which most blood cells originate. As white blood cells are believed to play a role in fighting infections, healthy bone marrow is essential for good health.

JOSHUA

Four-year-old Joshua Whymark is the only person in England with a condition called PNP, an enzyme deficiency which prevents his body from fighting infection. There have only ever been 33 known cases in the world and 29 of them have died.

The immunology unit at Great Ormond Street offered Joshua the chance of a bone marrow transplant, his only hope for a normal life. But as none of his immediate family – his mother, father or elder sister Vicky – had a bone marrow that matched, he was dependent upon an anonymous donor being found whose tissue closely enough matched his own. However, when a donor is unrelated, there is a 20 per cent risk of something going wrong. As the procedure is still fairly new, bone marrow transplant specialists may sometimes find that what seemed a good match at the time isn't a good match at all. Few hospitals other than Great Ormond Street even attempt such transplants.

Joshua, who lives with his divorced mother Sue and six-year-old sister Vicky in Southampton, was only discovered to have his serious enzyme deficiency after he caught chicken pox from his sister at the age of two. 'Instead of getting better in the normal way, he got worse and worse,' recalls Sue. 'More and more spots kept coming out and he couldn't eat or drink. His mouth was so sore he couldn't even suck his dummy.' Local doctors could only think it was a severe form of a usually mild infection and prescribed acylovir, a drug for the relief of symptoms with infections such as chicken pox. It was only when suddenly he could hardly breathe that he was rushed to hospital and diagnosed as having pneumonia.

After emergency treatment in intensive care, Joshua was off the danger list but the consultant realised something more serious was wrong and referred Joshua to Great Ormond Street. It was there that PNP was finally diagnosed.

For Sue, a lot of things started to make rather sad sense. Joshua had always been ill as a baby, with repeated bouts of hay fever, ear infections and stomach problems. At 11 months he had been diagnosed with mild cerebral palsy, which she now knows is associated with PNP.

'I was devastated by the cerebral palsy,' she said, 'but when they threw PNP at me as well, I thought it was the end of the world.' Sue has had to cope alone since Joshua was six weeks old.

The immediate effect of the new diagnosis was that Joshua – and Sue – had to become increasingly isolated, to avoid Joshua being exposed to any sort of infection.

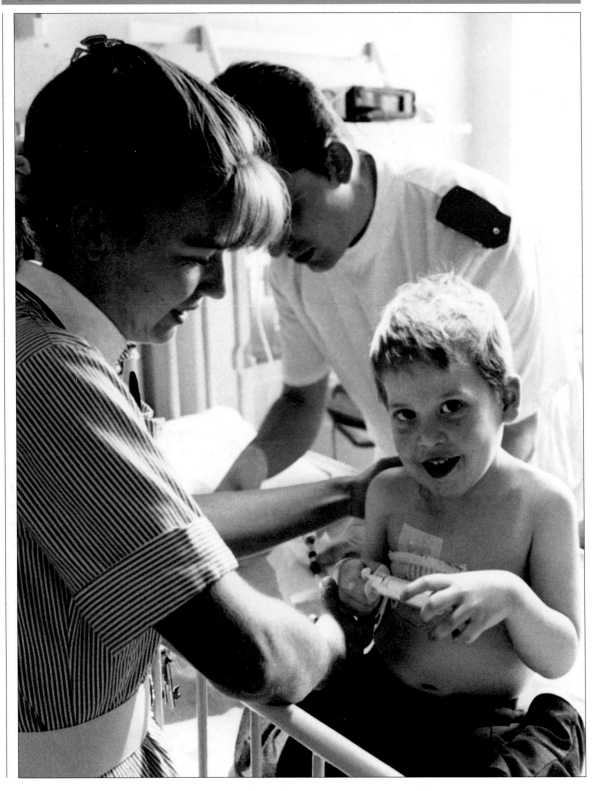

'Gradually, with each visit to Great Ormond Street, where Joshua was given an infusion of antibody to help give him a little resistance, I was told to withdraw more and more from our ordinary life: to stop going to the child development centre we were attending for Joshua's cerebral palsy, to avoid places with lots of people, to be careful at the shops. The risk that Joshua might catch an infection was just too big.'

For the next year, Joshua was largely confined to home and garden. 'But life was so busy that we just had to get on with it,' says Sue. Professionals now had to come to her. Every day there were speech therapy and physiotherapy sessions amongst other appointments and, with a house to run and another child to look after, there wasn't much time for Sue to dwell on loneliness. Added to that there were repeated visits to Great Ormond Street just to give blood. The blood had to be very fresh for testing for a donor match and Joshua's condition affected his blood in a way that often prevented accurate testing.

When the tests were finally complete and a suitable donor found, the day arrived for Joshua to come into hospital to be prepared for his bone marrow transplant. Vicky went to stay with her maternal grandparents so that Sue could be with Joshua at Great Ormond Street.

First, the transplant team, led by consultant Dr Paul Veys, removed just 3 per cent of Joshua's own marrow, under general anaesthetic, for freezing. This is all that is needed to be put back into his body, should the new marrow cease to work for him at any time in his life. It would bring him back to square one with a poor immune system, but would temporarily save his life. Then, for a fortnight, Joshua received daily amounts of extremely strong drugs, through a line direct to his heart, to kill off what was left of his own immune system – the white blood cells which defend the body – to prevent it trying to fight off the new bone marrow when it was inserted. But this left Joshua completely vulnerable to infection so, once his white-cell count had fallen sufficiently low, he had to be nursed in an isolation cubicle, which only staff and Sue could enter. It was a painful and difficult time.

'Yet Joshua was amazing through everything,' says Sue. 'Even when he was at his lowest he still always had a smile for the doctors and nurses.'

On the day Joshua was ready for the new bone marrow, the anonymous donor had his bone marrow harvested in another hospital. The marrow was then driven to Great Ormond Street and processed in the laboratory before being given to Joshua from a bag attached to a drip at his bedside. The nurse commented to Joshua that it looked like apple juice.

Joshua never questioned his long stay in hospital, nor the complex medical procedures he had to cope with. Unfortunately, he has been familiar with this sort of thing for most of his life.

65

'It wasn't an anticlimax and yet the actual bone marrow transplant wasn't as big a step as I'd previously thought it would be. But though what happened might not have seemed much, it made me very thoughtful because so very much depended upon it,' says Sue.

It was only afterwards doctors told her that Joshua is the only child in the world with PNP whose bone marrow transplant seems to have been successful with an unrelated donor.

'I can't really describe how I feel about the man who gave his bone marrow to Joshua,' says Sue. 'I hope some day I can meet him, if he agrees, but he has to stay anonymous to us for a year.'

Joshua and Sue left Great Ormond Street shortly after, but life couldn't start to be normal just yet. 'We were sent home with the same restrictions, if not stricter. They like you to remain as isolated as possible for the next six months, so although you think it's over, it isn't,' Sue explains.

'The next two weeks were like having a new baby. I was never dressed before 11am. There was a health visitor calling, a nurse coming to take Joshua's blood pressure daily and various people coming for his exercises and speech therapy, amongst other things. But Joshua never asked "why" about any of it. All this sort of thing is all just so much part of his life.'

Sue hopes that six months after the operation she will be told that Joshua can mix normally for the first time in his life. She just can't wait for that day. Her plan is to start him at Vicky's school as, since his return home from hospital, he has literally progressed in leaps and bounds. The boy whose cerebral palsy only allowed him to walk with a walking frame in hospital can now walk, at the time of writing, the quarter mile to his sister's school just holding on to a hand.

'It's the leap we've been working towards for three years,' says Sue proudly. 'Like other children with special needs, he'll need an assistant at school, but intellectually there's nothing he couldn't cope with. In many ways, with all he has been through, he is far more mature than other four year olds.'

A year after his transplant, if all has gone well, the new bone marrow will be strong enough to allow Joshua to receive all the usual childhood vaccinations. After two years, it should be up to its full strength, and life could be normal for the first time since Joshua's birth.

'It will mean I too can have my life back,' says Sue. 'It will be wonderful just to be able to see friends again and catch up with all that is going on in the outside world.'

JAY

Three-year-old Jay Williams was a patient on the infectious diseases unit.

At the age of 18 months, he caught bacterial meningitis, a serious infection of the brain and the membranes covering the spinal cord, but was fortunate enough to recover with no ill effects. When he caught it again at the age of three and again recovered, doctors at his local hospital in Eastbourne said that his predicament was rare. He was only the second child they had ever seen get meningitis twice, and they believed there was no way that he would ever get it again.

Within two weeks, Jay was struck down with his third attack and two days later his distraught parents, Dionne and Owen, with their four-month-old baby Danny, were making their way with Jay by ambulance to Great Ormond Street. Understandably, they were terrified that Jay would not come through a third bout with his brain and body unscathed.

'Jay was always a very lively boy, always running about. The first time it happened he just lay around all day and didn't like the light. His temperature was rising and rising,' says Dionne. The doctor made a home visit and suspected meningitis but there were no clear signs and it wasn't until later,

Jay is now well, but it was a worrying time for his mum, Dionne, especially with a young baby to look after at the same time.

when Dionne reported that Jay's neck had become rigid, that he was rushed into hospital for treatment.

'The second time, Jay didn't want to get out of bed one morning and I just had an awful feeling it was meningitis again,' says Dionne. This time he was kept in hospital on antibiotics for 14 days instead of ten. Nine days later Jay had his worst attack. 'He was in shock and he was fitting. We were absolutely terrified.'

At Great Ormond Street Jay was put on high doses of very powerful antibiotics, given a number of tests, an X-ray and a total body scan. An infected cyst was revealed, growing on his spine. He would need an

The mystery of Jay's repeated bouts of meningitis has now been solved, but doctors will continue to keep an eye on the cyst in his spine for some time to come.

operation to remove it but there was a risk because the nerves of the spinal cord were involved and there was a slight chance that surgery might leave his legs paralysed.

Neurosurgeon Mr David Peterson, who had never carried out this operation before in conjunction with meningitis, explained that Jay was probably born with an abnormal track of skin creating a connection between the skin and the inside of the spinal canal. This was what was allowing bacteria to enter the spinal canal and cause meningitis.

Some alarm bells were now ringing for Dionne. At six months, Jay had suddenly developed a big blistered lump – an abscess – at the base of his spine which was immediately removed. Dionne had noticed a lumpy area on his spine ever afterwards but had been assured it was probably scar tissue.

The operation to remove the cyst was successful, with no ill effects on Jay's legs, and the abnormal access to the spinal cord was also removed, so that he should never suffer meningitis again. But another shock was waiting. After the cyst was analysed in the laboratory, it was found that Jay also had tuberculosis. As all his family were then tested and found negative, it remains a mystery to this day how he contracted it.

Jay is still undergoing drug treatment for the TB, which will last 18 months, but is otherwise normal and healthy. 'No one looking at him can believe he went through so much,' says Dionne. However the cyst on his spine seems to be growing back and doctors at Great Ormond Street are keeping a check on it. 'I believe its position makes removal a bit dodgy so treatment at present is with the anti-tuberculosis drugs,' she says. 'We just have to hope and pray that it isn't going to be a problem.'

TARANDEEP

Five-year-old Tarandeep was another sufferer from an unusual infectious disease. He ended up at Great Ormond Street when, following a visit to family in India, he started suffering convulsions.

Tarandeep was rushed to hospital where he was given a brain scan. This revealed, in his head, the larvae of a tapeworm usually found in pork. The larvae were attacking his brain and causing cysts to form.

Tarandeep remained perky and cheerful throughout the investigations and drug treatment to kill off the larvae. A second scan showed that the cysts were disappearing and that Tarandeep was out of danger.

His family, practising Sikhs, remain mystified by the whole affair.

'We don't even eat pork!' says his father.

PLASTIC SURGERY

Although the term plastic surgery is commonly used in medicine, it tends to conjure up images of cosmetic techniques that are only skin deep. 'Reconstructive' surgery is perhaps a more accurate description.

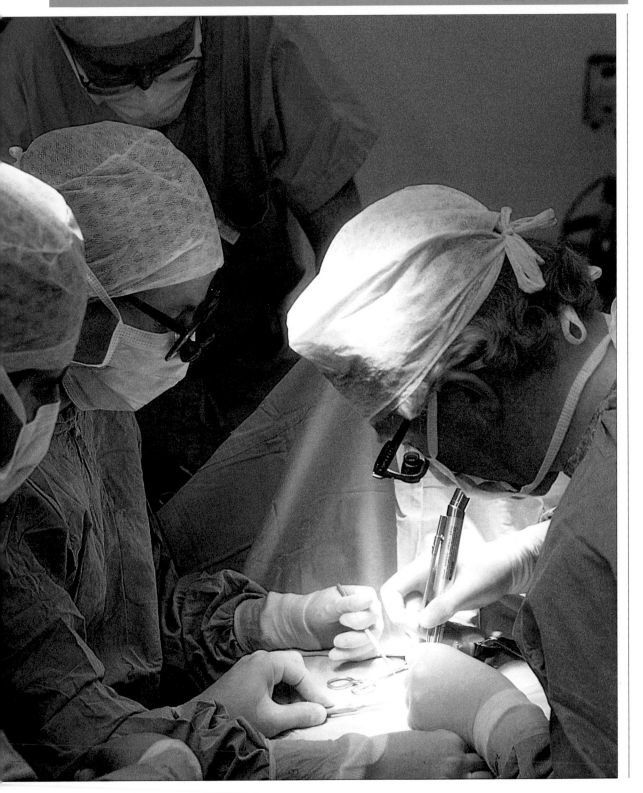

Surgery can help with rebuilding every part of the body, whether as a result of injury, disease (such as cancer) or congenital abnormalities: that is, those present since birth, such as a cleft palate. And while adequate skin coverage and repair is essential in almost every case, the delicate reorganisation of bones, blood vessels, nerves, muscles and tendons is at the heart of the process.

It is a discipline that requires an enormous amount of training. After five years of medical school, a plastic surgeon usually undergoes a minimum of four years' general surgical training, followed by at least five years of specialisation in reconstructive work, before being adequately qualified or experienced.

Great Ormond Street goes a few steps further. 'We are a supra regional specialist centre,' says surgeon Mr Paul Smith, who deals specifically with surgery on hands. 'We don't deal with everyday problems. Although there is some general work that comes from other wards of the hospital, this department has four main areas of work: hands, craniofacial [head and face] abnormalities, cleft lips and palates, and ear reconstruction. Each of these is almost a speciality in itself, and we are well known to consultants who refer appropriate patients on to us from all over the country.'

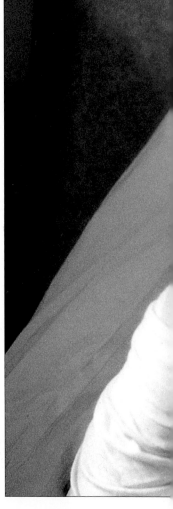

WAYNE

It seems unlikely that Mickey Mouse and a highly specialised plastic surgeon would have much in common, but on at least one occasion, Mickey has been an invaluable help to Mr Smith when reassuring a young patient's parent. Three-year-old Wayne Brown was born without any bones in the thumb on his right hand, and he was not able to grip with it.

As Mr Smith points out, the seemingly minor defect of a useless thumb is actually quite a major disability. Wayne couldn't hold a pencil properly. The simple requirements of daily living, such as buttoning up clothes, were also very difficult if not impossible for him to perform, although he tried to use his index finger as a thumb.

Wayne's mother Navelette was extremely keen for surgery to go ahead as soon as possible because she didn't want Wayne to be teased when he got to school.

Mr Smith's plan was to move Wayne's index finger into the thumb's position where, to all intents and purposes, it would

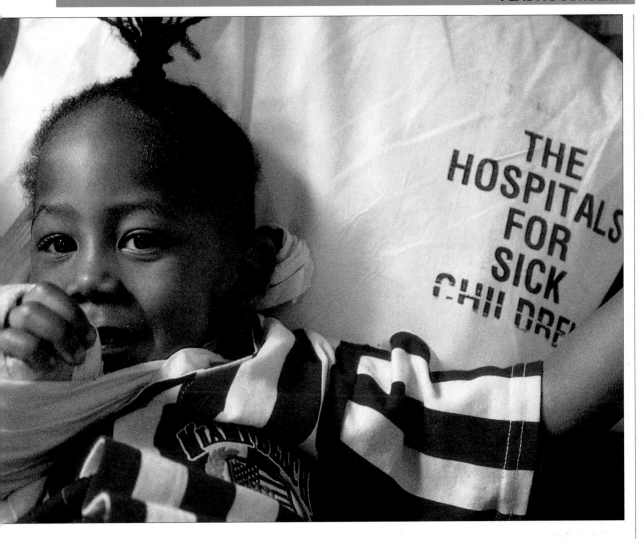

THE
HOSPITALS
FOR
SICK
CHILDRE

look and function like a thumb. Wayne would then have three fingers on that hand and one thumb. However, most people wouldn't even notice, he assured Wayne and his mother because the arrangement of the hand would be normal, with fingers and an opposing thumb, instead of abnormal, with four fingers and virtually no thumb. And when Mr Smith showed that Mickey Mouse has three fingers and one thumb on both hands, his mother was much cheered.

This sort of operation forms a major part of Mr Smith's work. Some children have hands that fail to develop: where fingers, thumbs or parts of the hand are missing or do not function properly. An alternative can sometimes be substituted: another finger, or even a toe. There are also cases where digits are duplicated, so some have to be removed and the remainder reorganised.

Although Wayne is a little older than most children who have this sort of operation, he will learn to use his new hand as a matter of course.

Left: Mr Smith specialises in surgery on hands.

73

If possible, Mr Smith's patients are usually a little younger than Wayne. It is preferable to make alterations before the peripheral nerves have become fully developed, which occurs at around the age of two. If an operation is carried out after that age, the child has to un-learn ways of moving or operating, and re-learn the way to use a new hand. It is usually easier for them to have a problem adjusted before they can really remember things being any different.

In Wayne's case, the operation took two hours, during which a delicate web of nerves, tendons and blood vessels had to be carefully moved in order to allow the repositioning of his finger. When the bandages were removed three weeks later, Wayne and his three sisters were amazed by the result. Although the new thumb was scarred and swollen, with the help of physiotherapy it would soon look and work just like his other one.

CARON

Seventeen-year-old Caron Curran has been a patient at Great Ormond Street since she was ten days old, when orthodontist Dr Michael Mars first took moulds of her mouth. Caron was born with a cleft lip and palate, and her first operation, at three months, was to repair the lip, enabling her to feed more easily.

Over the years she has had a number of operations: one at 16 months and another at two and a half years old, to close the palate; operations to insert grommets and later a T-tube to open the ear canal, because she had the hearing problems that often occur with a cleft lip and palate; an operation on her nose which was, and still is to some degree, flat on the side where the cleft was; and various operations to bring her teeth through in the proper places.

Her biggest operation was carried out just recently to bring the upper and lower jaw forward to correct her bite. To do this, her jaw was broken and her palate cut, and she had to wear a head brace, like a metal halo, for nine and a half weeks. She soon faces another operation for her nose, to improve its appearance, and another operation on her palate, to close some remaining holes.

Although so many operations have been necessary, Dr Mars took the view that the fewer major ones the better while Caron was very young. This was because the nearer her features were to their final shape, the more satisfactory the cosmetic outcome of the operations would be. It has meant, however, that she has had to cope through her childhood, and during the turbulent time of adolescence, with looking different from

Wayne's family – including his three older sisters – have been behind him all the way.

75

until adulthood – all three of them unanimously chose surgery now.

'We weighed everything up,' said Grant's mother, Alison. 'An operation now meant he would miss half a term at school. But as an adult it takes longer to recover and it might well mean missing a year of university. We've known of friends' children who took time out of university and then never went back, and that worried us for Grant's sake, especially as at present he is very keen to be a doctor.

'The other important factor for us was being told by the plastic surgeon, Mr Barry Jones, that children with facial problems often become very introverted. Grant is very extrovert and lively, so perhaps it wouldn't have happened, but I wouldn't want his personality changed for anything.'

The deciding factor was that Grant himself wanted the operation done sooner rather than later, although he has long been able to handle looking different. He had already had one operation, three years previ-

Because the shape of Grant's face had been changed by the surgery, his mouth had also altered and dental work was necessary.

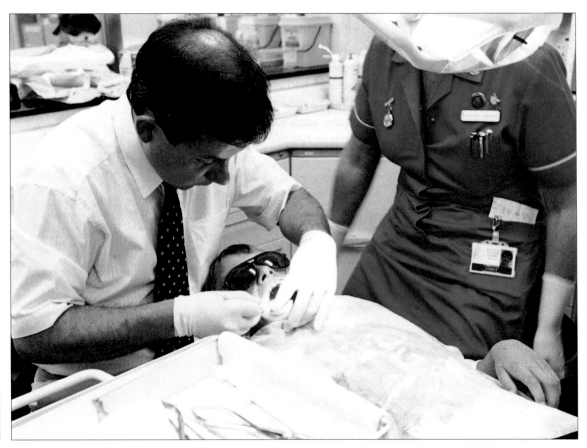

ously, to remodel his skull to take pressure off his brain, and he knows he may at some time need another, albeit more minor than the surgery he was opting for now.

The operation, performed by Mr Jones, was technically extremely complex, involving peeling the face forward to get to the bone, building up the cheekbones with bone from Grant's hip, keeping them in place with nuts and bolts and putting a new piece of bone in his nose. Such an assault inevitably causes heavy bruising, which doesn't disappear entirely until about six months afterwards. But to Grant, the positive effects were quickly gratifying.

'He thinks it is really funny when people don't recognise him. He is really glad he has had the operation done,' says Alison. 'As for me, I didn't think he looked particularly abnormal before the operation – when it's your own child, you don't think there's anything wrong with them – but now I can see what I didn't see before. I look at him asleep and think, "Oh yes, you do look different."'

For six weeks after surgery Grant was obliged to eat a soft diet and he couldn't ride his bike. But hardest for him to handle is not being able to play contact sports for a year as he is a keen rugby player.

His feelings about his operation are succinctly summed up in this (abridged) piece he wrote for a class project at school on the subject of something important that had recently happened.

'On August l4th I had an operation which changed my face forever . . . It is two months later and I am still getting used to my new face . . . I look in the mirror every morning and I think "who's that?" and then I remember "it's me!!" My face has changed but I haven't. Inside I am still Grant. The worst thing about everything that has happened to me in the last eight weeks is that I'm not allowed to play sport.'

In 1994 scientists at the Institute of Child Health, the research arm of Great Ormond Street, traced the cause of Crouzon Syndrome to a specific gene. The team is now hopeful that the discovery could eventually lead to earlier treatment and ultimately prevention of the disease.

Alison says: 'By the time Grant grows up and wants children himself, hopefully doctors will be able to do something so that others don't have to go through what Grant has been through.'

The complex surgery needed to change Grant's face caused heavy bruising, but now that he has recovered he is glad that the operation was done.

7

HEART DISEASE

Despite all the emotional capabilities we attribute to our hearts in colloquial language, the human heart has just one function: to pump blood around the body, from the veins into the arteries. Described very simply, heart disease is its failure to do so – but this lack of function can have many causes.

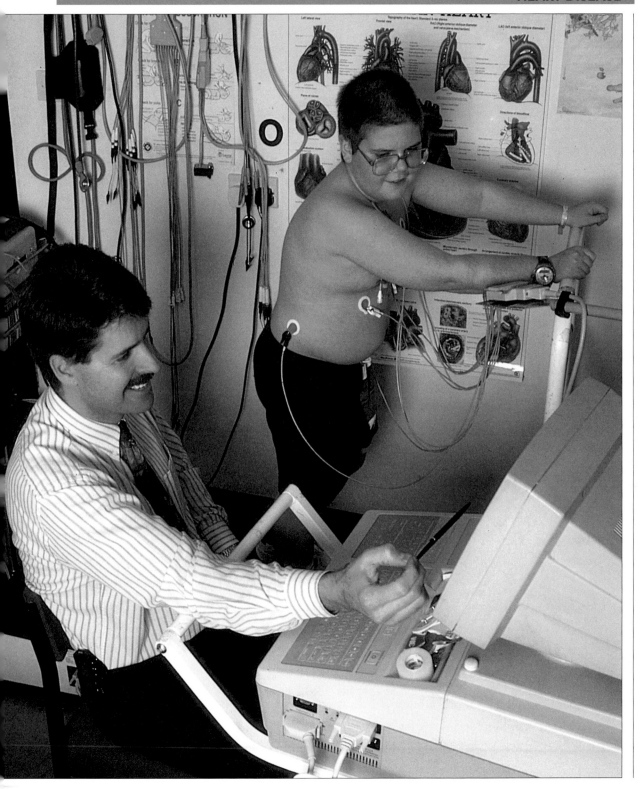

Currently, about 50 per cent of British adults die from heart disease. However this disease is almost always an acquired form, influenced by a variety of habits including a poor diet, smoking and lack of physical exercise.

On the other hand, children who suffer from heart disease have not yet had time to acquire destructive habits, or for their bodies to degenerate with age. The problems they face are more usually those they are born with, such as faulty construction of the heart or arteries. In fact, such congenital abnormalities can affect nearly one in each hundred children born in Britain today.

The cardiac unit at Great Ormond Street specialises in the treatment of children with complex heart disease, from the new-born to teenagers and operates on about 700 children per year. 'Many of them require surgery,' says cardiologist Dr John Deanfield, 'although in the last few years it has become possible to treat some of them without surgery by what's called Interventional Cardiac Catheterisation.' This is a technique for correcting defects in the heart, where a catheter is inserted into the heart without opening up the chest cavity, such as stretching a heart valve, with a small balloon located on the end of the catheter.

SANA

The case of Sana Din, a new-born baby, illustrates how certain cardiac techniques have progressed in recent years. Sana was born at a hospital in west London, but was rushed to Great Ormond Street immediately after her birth because her lungs couldn't supply her body with sufficient oxygen. There, surgeons quickly identified the problem.

Her two main arteries – the aorta, which leads from the left chamber of the heart and takes oxygen-rich blood to the body, and the pulmonary artery, which comes from the right chamber and takes blood to the lungs to collect oxygen – were connected the wrong way round. So blood from which the oxygen had been used up was being sent around the body again but with little oxygen in it, while blood supplied with oxygen by the lungs just uselessly went back to the lungs again.

To keep Sana alive, cardiologists made a temporary hole in her heart with a catheter (to allow oxygenated blood into the correct side of the heart). Later, surgeons arranged to carry out open-heart surgery – to switch the arteries around – when she was ten days old. Without these treatments, Sana would soon have died.

Switching arteries like this is a procedure which has been carried out successfully for more than ten years, with relatively low risk of death or brain damage. But, as heart surgeon Mr Martin Elliott points out, a five-per-cent risk is not much better than a 50-per-cent-risk to the family involved, as they still don't know until it is all over whether their own child will be one of the majority to survive. It was to be an anxious wait for Sana's mother and father, Fatzila and Nassir.

This type of operation usually lasts between four and six hours. For the surgeons, magnifying glasses and a strong light are essential, as a baby's heart is no bigger than a walnut. It is the development of better anaesthetics and bypass technology, to do the work of the heart and lungs while the surgeon works, that has allowed heart surgery on babies to progress dramatically in recent years. In this case, not only did Sana's main arteries need to be switched but, more complicatedly, so did the tiny coronary arteries which supply the heart itself with blood.

Without the development of heart-bypass surgery over the last ten years or so, Sana would not have lived very long.

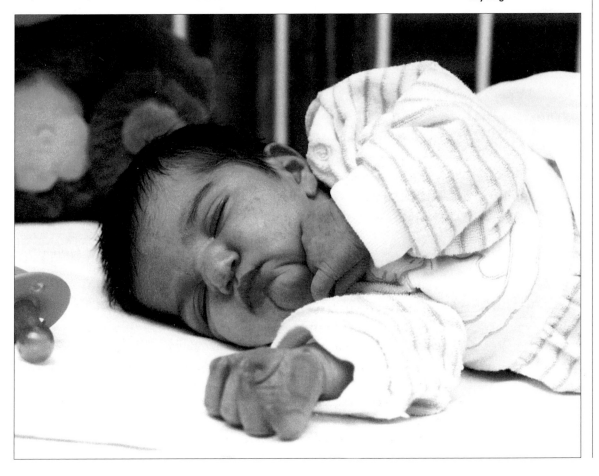

Despite her dramatic start in life, Sana should never need further heart surgery.

Thankfully, immediately after the operation, Sana's heart started functioning normally. After a short stay in intensive care and then a week on an ordinary ward, she was ready to go home. Her circulation was checked by an ultrasound machine called ECHO. (Ultrasound is also used for scans of pregnant women.) This ultra-modern and highly sensitive piece of equipment – paid for entirely by private donations – was able to show not only the make-up of Sana's new circulation but exactly how well her blood was flowing.

In previous years it was thought that tiny babies such as Sana were just too young to undergo such major surgery successfully. But results are now starting to show that the earlier such an operation is performed, the better the outcome. Throughout her childhood and adolescence, Sana will return to Great Ormond Street both for checks on her progress and for essential long-term feedback – to give the doctors an idea of how her heart is functioning. She should never need another operation on her heart.

NEAL

Frequent visits to Great Ormond Street are a fact of life for 14-year-old Neal Wilson, who lives with his parents, Geraldine and Alan, and sister Nina in Bournemouth.

Neal was born with part of the right side of his heart missing – not the sort of problem that could be rectified immediately as in Sana's case – and has had to undergo several operations to keep him well. The first took place when he was four days old, when surgeons inserted a cardiac shunt, a temporary measure so that additional blood could be directed through to his right lung to pick up oxygen.

Geraldine and Alan knew that Neal faced further surgery at a few years old to try to correct the problem in a more permanent way.

'It was a very worrying time, of course,' recalls Geraldine. 'Even as a toddler he still looked exceedingly blue but we made the conscious decision not to treat him as an invalid. He did everything a normal toddler would do and nothing untoward occurred.'

When Neal was three he underwent his first major open-heart surgery at Great Ormond Street.

'The doctors have always been very above board. They told us they thought more surgery was likely after that, but didn't know when. So we thought, well, Neal's fine at the moment so we'll just go along with it,' says Geraldine. 'Neal has always done everything everyone else does but he just has to stop a bit sooner because his threshold is lower,' says Alan. However, by the age of 14, Neal himself no longer felt he could keep up.

'My friends all noticed it too,' he explains, adding that 'I could do hardly anything that I could do two years ago. I was getting tired and breathless quickly.' Cold also really affected him and stopped him doing many things he wanted to do. He was wearing extra layers of clothing and two pairs of socks even in the summer.

Over the years Neal has remained a regular at the cardiac clinic, for observation, tests and scans, and Dr Philip Rees, his cardiologist, has known him since he was a baby. So it was Dr Rees that Neal and his father recently came to see to discuss the wisdom of a third operation. Neal, says Dr Rees, had a 90 per cent chance of successfully coming through the type of operation he would need – but that is a far higher risk than for a more usual cardiac operation on a 14 year old. While Dr Rees wasn't sure he could justify the odds, for Neal the issues were different. He wanted to undergo an operation if it would let him feel even only a little better again.

An X-ray film, viewed and discussed by Dr Rees and his colleague Mr Marc de Leval, one of the world's top surgeons from Belgium, decided the matter. A chamber on the right of Neal's heart was now dangerously stretched. His condition could at some stage become fatal if surgery was not carried out. An operation date was set.

Mr de Leval is an internationally renowned researcher on the type of surgery needed by Neal. His task was to create artificial channels around the heart – by joining the upper and lower veins through the heart – through which Neal's blood could be diverted. First, bypass machines had to take over the work of Neal's heart and lungs but even achieving this took two-and-a-half hours, because scarring from previous surgery made it difficult to gain any access to the relevant veins and arteries.

Most of the operation was performed without stopping Neal's heart because the longer the heart is stopped, the greater the danger – and this was to be a long operation. Once on bypass, the surgeon created new channels for Neal's blood using a special plastic material called Goretex. He reduced the size of the defective right chamber of Neal's heart, to make it smaller and more efficient. In all, this complicated surgery took nearly nine hours.

As a result of the operation, Neal is beginning to have a little more

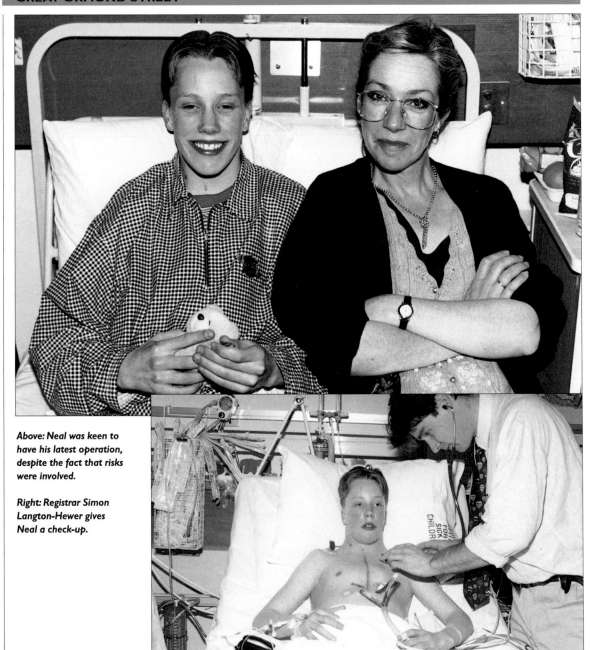

Above: Neal was keen to have his latest operation, despite the fact that risks were involved.

Right: Registrar Simon Langton-Hewer gives Neal a check-up.

energy and stamina, but it hasn't all been plain sailing since he recovered from the operation. Not long after his surgery he had to be rushed back to Great Ormond Street with blood rushing to his head and a racing heartbeat. 'It was a horrible and frightening feeling,' he says. A scan showed nothing wrong and a small electric charge to his heart (a tenth of the amount required for an adult in cardiac arrest), given under general anaesthetic, steadied it again. Since then the 'atrial flutter', as it is termed, has happened more than once but, as Neal comments, 'I'm used to them now'.

'They are just a nuisance really. Neal's on three drugs to regulate his heart and it is probably just a case of fine tuning,' says Alan. 'We take each day as it comes. I don't see any point in worrying about anything until we're told to. And I always thought he would be fine. Obviously, we had great faith in the medical team.'

FINDING OUT MORE

Despite the expertise that now exists for treating patients such as Neal, treatment of children with heart disease may operate very differently in the future. 'We are developing a new type of cardiology, says Dr Deanfield, 'looking at preventative measures, rather than "damage limitation".'

By studying several thousand children, from the age of five upwards, Dr Deanfield and his colleages are investigating the development of acquired heart disease, and have found that, alarmingly, the process begins in childhood. Factors that influence us before we are born, in childhood and adolescence all contribute to the varieties of heart disease that will eventually kill every second person. For example, inherited and environmental factors, how much exercise we take and whether or not we smoke as adolescents all have a bearing on developing heart disease in later life.

Still further work – for congenital abnormalities – comes within pre-natal care. Ultrasound equipment, used for routine scans of pregnant women, is now so powerful that heart defects can be seen in foetuses which are only 16 to 18 weeks old. This allows a whole range of responses. If parents are worried about whether their baby's heart is developing normally, they can be reassured. Alternatively, if a severe problem is present, parents may wish to terminate the pregnancy. Or if an abnormality is known to be present and the pregnancy goes ahead, it is possible to plan in advance what to do when the baby is born.

'Although we can now treat many heart defects that used to be fatal in the past,' says Dr Deanfield, 'we are only looking at the "first generation" of survivors. We are only just finding out how they are going to get on, and about the results of our work in the past.'

Here is research and pioneering medicine at its best. Its results affect not just the children who walk through the doors of Great Ormond Street, but the whole population.

8 PLAY AND SCHOOLING

Every day at Great Ormond Street brings something different and, although there are routines, life is never predictable. The hospital wards become the children's new homes away from the world outside, but they are kept in touch by the play specialists and teachers who work on every ward. Once children are fit enough, they can also escape to the normality provided by the play centre and the Children's Hospital School – two much-loved havens on the ground floor.

Few illnesses are so strong that they can prevent a child from playing or learning. No matter how crippling or painful their condition, each will find some way to use their imagination to enter another world and take their mind off their illness. The play rooms on the wards are stacked high with games, toys, books and train sets, so there is always a useful distraction nearby.

Lesley Wilson is one of 37 play specialists at Great Ormond Street; an expert figure of fun, with the job of introducing laughter and dissipating what, for some children, can be the terror of a hospital ward. She has been at Great Ormond Street for over 13 years, but is still filled with enthusiasm. 'Working with children here is the most rewarding thing I have ever done,' she says. 'I still wake up on Monday morning, thinking: "Great. It's the start of another week."'

The play specialist's main task is to provide diversionary and therapeutic tactics that ease the stay of the children in hospital and aid their recovery. So instead of needles and pain, Lesley and her colleagues bring games, colouring books, fun and a healthy dose of normality to the children who have come to regard ventilators and dialysis machines as everyday furniture.

'My job is to give the children back their childhood,' says Lesley. 'Some of the kids here have known no life outside this hospital. They have begun to think that every child grows up in this way. But even in these surroundings they are all still children, and I have the wonderful task of letting them be themselves. Nothing gives me a greater thrill than watching the face of a sick child light up when they see me on my way to visit them.' With such irresistible medicine, it is hardly surprising that Lesley and all the play specialists are so popular.

A key role of the play specialists is to work closely with the other ward staff and, as required, gently help children to understand more about their condition and prepare them for operations. With subtle direction, play can be used to explain complex and often frightening medical procedures to children who are too young to understand in any other way. The specialists also help children to relax when they are waiting in outpatients or for an X-ray.

ESCAPING FROM THE WARDS

A change of environment helps many of the children who are bored with being confined to bed, and children can go to the play centre downstairs and have fun alongside their brothers and sisters, as well as children from most of the other wards.

There is something here to keep everyone happy: new people to play with and lots of toys generously provided by the Friends of Great Ormond Street, manufacturers and individual well-wishers. Ros Love, the Group Play Co-ordinator, is extremely grateful that the hospital receives enough gifts at Christmas to enable every patient to be given a suitable birthday present during the following year. The play specialists and nurses try to arrange birthday parties for children and will always invite the teachers from the school to join in the fun if they can spare the time.

The play centre is an almost medical-free zone. There are no doctors, no injections, and nurses are only present if they have brought down children who need to be accompanied – perhaps because they are on a ventilator or a drip. Parents are also welcome but many take the opportunity of having five minutes off while their children are enjoying themselves.

Different parts of the play centre are devoted to various stimulating activities. One room is set aside for older children who can play computer games, or watch TV or a video. Elsewhere, younger ones can let themselves go with messy creativity. Playing with paint, water, spaghetti, shaving foam or custard is enjoyed with particular enthusiasm because it is the antithesis of hospital life.

IMAGINING LIFE AT HOME

At the back of the play room is the home corner: a toy version of a grown-up kitchen, complete with a toy cooker, dining table, chairs and real child-height sink, as well as the toy cups, saucers and teapot that all children need for a make-believe tea party.

Any child outside the hospital would see it as just another area of potential fun, but for the children at Great Ormond Street, this little corner filled with plastic furniture is one of their strongest links with home. Here, they can re-invent their own existence, acting out all of the things they have seen their mums and dads doing. They pretend to wash the dishes, cook, iron clothes, make the tea and put their teddy bears to bed just as healthy children do. Occasionally, children will pretend to be parents, speaking to imaginary children who live in an imaginary house, just like the one they remember as home.

Says Lesley: 'As weeks sometimes move into months, this simple act provides them with a strong link to the life they have known outside. It is also a chance for us to pick up things that have happened to that child at

'Working with children here is the most rewarding thing I have ever done . . .'

LESLEY WILSON

home. Very occasionally, we come across emotionally disturbed children who we suspect may have been having a difficult time at home. Most are withdrawn and quiet, and very few will tell you about it during normal conversation, but the full story will often emerge during play. I remember after I had spent a lot of time with one little boy, he finally plucked up the courage to tell me how his dad had picked him up and thrown him down the stairs.'

PLAYING DOCTORS AND NURSES

Real syringes, catheters and other medical equipment which can be used safely during play are always on hand in the hospital corner. Children seem to enjoy being in control, administering treatment rather than having to endure it themselves.

In another section of the play room is a hospital corner, a little Wendy house equipped with all the furniture and features to be found in the child's own hospital ward. A tiny child-sized bed, complete with sheets and pillow, sits beside a locker and a light. All it needs is a patient. And that's where the teddy bears and dolls come in. Like many of the children, each of the cuddly toys seems to have undergone some form of medical treatment, because attached to their arms and chest are real surgical tubes, bandages and drips.

Some teddies and dolls will have had heart transplants, with a scar to

show for evidence. Others may have received chemotherapy, or a kidney transplant, have a leg in plaster or whatever condition might be experienced by a child. These are the toys used by play specialists to prepare the children for surgery. At Great Ormond Street, even the most complex operations can be explained by pretending that they are being performed on an ill teddy bear.

'It's a chance for us to tell the children what is going to happen to them,' explains Lesley, 'and using play can prevent them from becoming so frightened. It also allows the children to act out their worries and fears while remaining a little bit removed from it all. Often, the only way they will tell you what they are thinking is through play, but once you have found out why they are afraid, then you are well on your way to knowing what to do to put their minds at rest.'

Some children are so frightened of injections that even getting them to touch a syringe can be a problem. Once again, play comes to the rescue, and they are encouraged to squirt water or paint using one as a water pistol. As soon as they become familiar with it, the syringe becomes less terrifying.

SUPERMAN TO THE RESCUE

However, using preparation dolls and teddy bears also has its drawbacks. Some children will look back with scepticism when comparing their own experiences of surgery and needles with the benign image presented by stoical teddy bears. A few feel betrayed once they have experienced the painful reality of an operation and sometimes that feeling is enough to shatter the special relationship that exists between a boy and a bear, as Lesley Wilson once found out.

'I was asked to go to the home of a five-year-old who had an unsuccessful kidney transplant at Great Ormond Street. He was having nightmares, had become very aggressive towards his sister and was also having problems at school. He had never come to terms with what had happened to him, and was still on a dialysis machine. It was essential for him to overcome his fears so that he would be in the right psychological state for another attempt at a kidney transplant when he was older.

'I knew the little boy very well. At the age of three and a half, he became ill and an unsuccessful kidney transplant followed. By the time he was five, he knew all the medical terms related to his illness, and was a very deep thinker, so I realised that, despite his young age, he was going to ask me a lot of detailed questions. Getting my answers right was vital for his future, so I took with me a preparation teddy bear fitted with all the tubes and lines he would have had when he first awoke after his transplant.

'When I arrived, he was pleased to see me, and we played a few games before I introduced him to my adapted bear. Gently, I explained that the teddy had received a kidney transplant, but was still feeling sick, finally asking if the bear could stay in his house for a few weeks while it recovered from its operation.

'Before I could continue with my well-rehearsed lines, he took one dismissive look at the teddy and said bluntly: "Don't be stupid Lesley. Teddy bears don't have kidneys. How can this bear have had a kidney transplant? It doesn't need a kidney." I just wanted the floor to open up and swallow me but I managed to retrieve the situation by saying: "OK, most teddy bears don't have kidneys but this one is special." I could see that he was still a bit sceptical, but I pressed ahead nevertheless, and gradually, he began to take part in the story.

'As we talked, he touched some of the tubes and lines coming out of the bear and said: "Teddy bears don't like these tubes. They frighten them". By the end of the day, he was confident enough to take the drips out of one of the bear's arms and put them into the other. "The needle has tissued," he explained, meaning that it had become blocked, and the fluid could no longer flow into the vein. Exactly the same thing had happened after his operation.

'When I left his home I knew that my work with this boy was only just beginning and it would take a long time to get him to overcome his fears sufficiently to allow us to have another attempt at a transplant. As it turned out, he eventually rejected all communication about transplants via the teddy bear so I decided to invent some stories about Superman, one of his heroes. My Superman became ill while he was out on a mission one day and ended up needing dialysis. Of course, he could still do amazing feats, but occasionally his condition would make him feel weak and tired. Superman knew he needed a kidney transplant to restore his strength.

'Over the course of four or five chats, Superman began to perform miracles, and slowly, as each of my stories unfolded, the boy began to talk about his fears of a second transplant. But he always did it through Superman, never talking about himself. He would say things like: "Superman thinks dialysis is a nuisance because he can't play with his friends at lunch-time." He also told me how Superman didn't like going to

'Superman has had a kidney transplant and he can play football now.'

T R A N S P L A N T   P A T I E N T

hospital clinics every month, and hated having fluid put into his tummy through a tube. "It stops him from playing football," he said.

'As I left, I always asked him to draw a picture of Superman for my next visit. It was a way of getting him to think about everything we had talked through during our play-time. Usually, he depicted Superman with a dialysis tube in his tummy, but one day he drew him without a tube and explained "Superman has had a kidney transplant and he can play football now."

'After that I knew that Superman's magic had worked and the boy was now ready to face another transplant. Fifteen months later, he had his operation and this time it was a success. I still see him when he comes to the outpatient's clinic and he looks healthy, fit and full of energy. He has grown a lot, and I know that life is much better for him now that he is free from tubes, dialysis and fear. I'm glad too, that Superman and I played a small part in giving him his new life.'

The piano in the playroom can be used by children or visiting entertainers. It is part of the play facilities to help children do exactly what they want to do, and to try to forget about why they are in hospital.

DEALING WITH PROBLEMS

The play specialists have a very special relationship with the children they have known for months or years, and they often continue to work with those who return as outpatients for regular check-ups. They are particularly concerned for the children who have difficulty forming satisfactory relationships with others as often happens to those who have been hospital-bound for some of their life.

Many children show signs of being emotionally disturbed two or three years after their stay in hospital and they often develop love-hate relationships with their mothers. In their minds, she was the person who brought them to hospital in the first place and left them in the hands of the medical staff. But at the same time, they have very close bonds with their mother because, for so long, hers was the only familiar face among strangers. She was there to comfort and cuddle them, to dry their tears and tell them that everything was going to be all right.

BEHAVING LIKE CHILDREN

A number of the children in hospital have been utterly spoilt. Not surprisingly, some adults will give a child anything he or she wants in an attempt to compensate for the ordeal each has to go through. The staff at Great Ormond Street are just as prone to spoiling the children as any parent, because it makes them feel better too. However, difficulties do arise later in life. After years of commanding attention and being treated as special because they are ill, some of the children can become very demanding when they get better and lose their status as a sick child. In Lesley's view: 'Some of the children would drive you berserk. Many of them are little rascals by nature, but in a strange way, I find this reassuring because it reminds me that children will always be children no matter where they are.

'Expensive medical equipment mounted on stands with wheels is often grabbed by the kids who then race up and down the ward with it. Wheelchairs are a favourite, and sometimes the corridors here are like a

The hospital school tries to arrange its activities so that children of different age groups can be busy at the same time.

race track. Retaining discipline can be difficult, and occasionally, with the longer-stay children, we have to sit them down and draw up a programme of what is and what is not acceptable behaviour.

'Adolescents are usually the worst, and smoking on the balconies used to be a big problem. Others sometimes run away, and I can still remember the sight of a burly houseman sprinting after a sprightly 14 year old as he disappeared down the street outside the hospital for the third time that week. The poor boy was running simply because he was frightened, and he is not the only one to have acted out of fear. Others have locked themselves in toilets for hours rather than face their pre-med injections, often only emerging after much pleading from staff. It can cause disruption to theatre schedules, but we do understand their predicament.'

CONTINUITY AND NORMALITY

Away from all the medical bustle, a calm and peaceful atmosphere reigns in the Children's Hospital School. While the play centre, just down the corridor, provides valuable therapy and fun, the school ensures that children do not fall behind with their education and gives them a chance to receive individual tuition as well as a sense of stability.

Children with special needs, long-stay pupils and those coming up to exams are given special priority. The school will also take brothers and sisters of long-stay patients, if they have leave of absence from their home school, and tries to accommodate short-stay patients too, depending on numbers. The team of 10 full-time and four part-time staff and two music specialists teach children ranging from under five to late teens – and are occasionally helped out by students and volunteers.

Tables and desks are arranged so that children with different levels of ability can all attend classes at the same time without interrupting each other. At the far end is the well-stocked library and a TV, and there's a good selection of computers which can also be wheeled to the wards upstairs. There is always a lot going on in class, so there is a separate quiet room where teenagers can study without any interruptions.

It is very unusual for a child to cry at the school so if Head Teacher Yvonne Hill hears anyone in distress she immediately comes out of her office to find out the reason. She is full of encouragement and enthusiasm, ready to talk to a child even if she is giving one of the frequent stream of visitors a guided tour of the classroom. Generally, the staff are used to interruptions and don't let them stop their work although everything comes to a standstill when the guinea pigs arrive to be stroked.

A TYPICAL DAY

The teachers arrive at Great Ormond Street at 8.45. Staff are based in both the school room and on the wards throughout the hospital. They check which children can go down to the school room that day and which need to remain on the wards where they can still be helped on an individual basis. They always consult with the ward staff and play specialists and also let the children know about the activities in the school room. Sometimes teachers will employ gentle and firm persuasion because they know that even the most reluctant children are nearly always glad once they have made the effort to join in.

Most children get dressed so that they feel more normal – and for a short time they are simply at school and not in hospital. The school room session lasts for an hour and a half and follows a carefully structured plan in line with the National Curriculum. After lunch, those who are able can return to school for the afternoon workshops. These are run in close association with the play specialists so that there is always some form of activity for each age group and ability. So, for instance, on one afternoon, the play workshop for teenagers will coincide with the school's music session for the under-eights. The workshops give children a chance to be creative (perhaps making pizza in the school's kitchen or learning how to develop a photograph) and to work at their own pace and level.

School officially ends at 3.15 although the teachers often have to work later to finish everything that needs to be done. After this time, the children tend to start getting tired, don't want to miss children's TV and of course are looking forward to seeing their visitors.

A SCHOOL IN ANOTHER WORLD

Although the school has the same aim and function as any other, because it is sited within the hospital the teachers have a particularly caring attitude and have to cope with various special circumstances.

Unlike other schools, there is a large turnover of children. There is also a high intake of children from different cultures and the staff have put up signs in other languages to make these children feel more welcome. A teacher and play specialist are also now learning Arabic and Greek in their spare time.

All the staff are flexible because the children's medical needs have to come first. Sometimes the pupils can't go down to lessons because they are waiting for their consultant to visit them. Or they may be undergoing a rigorous physiotherapy regime (particularly on the rheumatology ward),

needing treatment for a couple of hours each day. Then the teachers will do their best to make sure patients don't miss out on school altogether. They adapt whenever they can for the benefit of the children – even though at times they feel like they are part of a giant jigsaw puzzle.

As well as the main play centre on the ground floor, each ward has a play room where children and their families can relax.

Because of their medical problems the children are not well enough to do PE or play outside team games, although some have the opportunity to learn dance. Recently, dancers from the Contemporary Dance Trust have achieved amazing success with children who have psychological illnesses and communication difficulties, enabling them to express themselves through movement and dance.

Once pupils leave the hospital, whenever possible the teachers continue links with their school at home, particularly if the child will be coming in again. Old pupils still remember and appreciate their teachers. Yvonne Hill, who has been at the school for ten years, often hears from former pupils and delights in their progress. For example, one girl who took her GCSEs at Great Ormond Street has now gone on to university. Success stories like this bring even more satisfaction to a thoroughly worthwhile job.

EATING PROBLEMS

Food and diet play an important role in every department at Great Ormond Street. Obviously, good nutrition is vital for children who are unwell, but problems concerning eating can take many forms, from simple loss of appetite to an inability to digest certain foods.

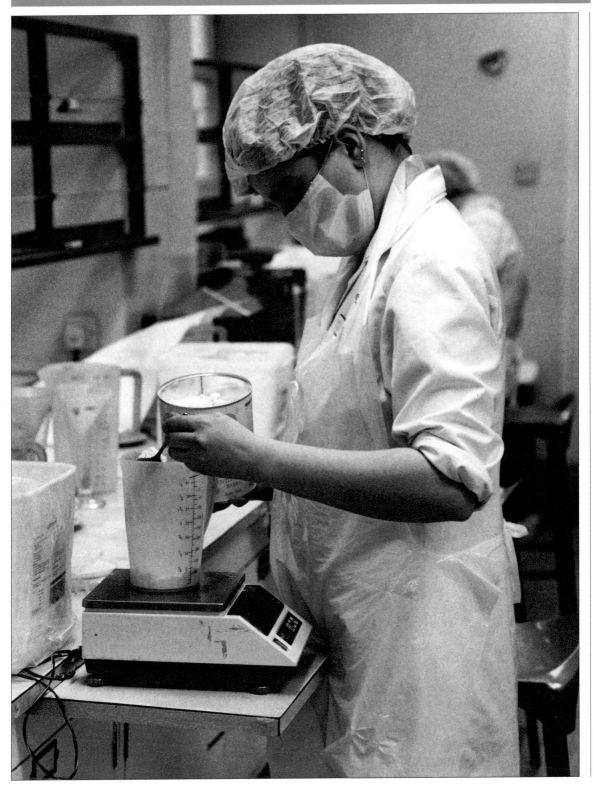

Someone who sees a wide range of patients is Chief Dietitian, Marjorie Dixon, one of 12 dietitians working throughout the hospital. They see babies and children with a variety of problems ranging from feeding difficulties to illnesses that required dietary modification as the main part of their treatment.

Some children simply dislike food. Almost everyone knows the feeling of losing their appetite when they are ill and children – especially those with a chronic illness – may feel so unwell that their appetite and food intake drop dramatically. Encouraging such children to eat, or increasing the nutritional content of the food they do want to eat, is part of the dietitian's role.

Other children have 'inborn errors of metabolism': an inability of the body to use certain nutrients in foods, such as protein, because they may lack a specific enzyme (a chemical normally produced by the body). Sometimes the problem nutrient can be broken down only partially, but not fully – as if there is a missing link in the chain of chemical reactions – sometimes resulting in toxic substances accumulating in the body.

'In these cases,' Marjorie Dixon says, 'we have to alter their diet to avoid the type of food that is making them ill.

'We also deal with many other conditions, such as children with kidney failure who need controlled amounts of protein and phosphate in their diet; and cystic fibrosis patients who have higher energy requirements. Some children need to be fed by a tube if they cannot take adequate nutrition by mouth, and we design the composition of the feeding solution.'

JAMIE

Five-year-old Jamie Berry is a firm favourite with many of the staff at Great Ormond Street. He was referred to them suffering from extremely complex problems with his digestive system and has spent, in his father's calculation, about 80 per cent of his life in hospital, while staff battled to find a way to get him healthy. His mother, Alison, lived there with him and, at a time when Jamie was in intensive care, his father, David, gave up his job and also came to stay at the hospital.

Jamie's condition was so complex that he was unable to tolerate large quantities of foods, especially hard foods such as bread, crisps, chips and sweets: the foods children love to eat! Instead he was encouraged to eat small portions of liquid foods including soup, jelly and custard. Also, he can become seriously dehydrated. This is because the muscles of his

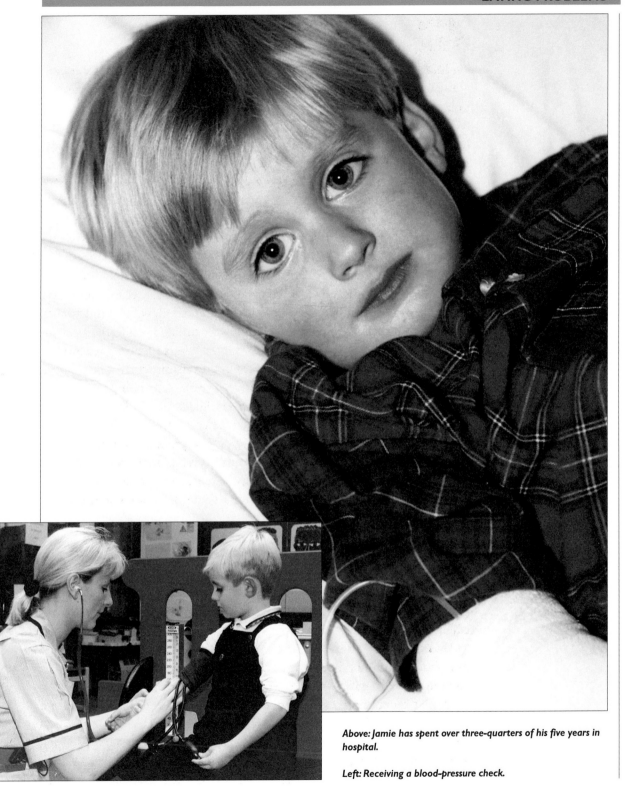

Above: Jamie has spent over three-quarters of his five years in hospital.

Left: Receiving a blood-pressure check.

intestines go into spasm when they contain food, and he cannot absorb any nutrients. There were many times that Jamie was not allowed to eat at all.

Jamie was so thin by the time he was two and a half that he came to Great Ormond Street for further tests and treatment. It was estimated that he would have to stay for between one week and three months. But it was to be over two years in and out of the hospital – 'like yo-yos', as Alison puts it.

When he was three, Jamie had an ileostomy, an operation to create an outlet for the small intestine through the wall of his stomach, so that the large intestine could be bypassed. Eventually his diet was based mostly

Most medical procedures are very familiar to Jamie, so it is almost inevitable that they emerge during play.

on a specialised liquid feed which was passed through a tube in his stomach, and it was expected that this method would successfully deliver the nutrition he needed. However his gut would unexpectedly twist or stop working so that often, after returning home, he would have to come back to the hospital for yet more treatment.

Unfortunately, Jamie did not thrive sufficiently on the liquid feed, which was pumped into his stomach overnight. 'I had to give him a litre and a half a day,' says Alison. 'That's an awful lot and he would often sick it back up again. Sometimes, in the morning, I would find that the tape securing the tube in his stomach had come off and so all the feed was in the bed and none in him! He never gained weight, couldn't run around and was lethargic and uncomfortable, because his tummy was always swollen. Yet on good days, he still managed to be happy.'

During his long hospital stays to sort out his many problems, Jamie was able to visit the play centre on the ground floor and, because most of the time he was having tests or being observed and was not necessarily confined to bed, his parents could take him out to parks and museums and the toy shops around Oxford Street.

But when Jamie became even more dehydrated and his stomach even more swollen, and no modifications seemed to improve matters, his doctors finally decided on total parenteral nutrition (TPN): a method of feeding a nutritious liquid directly into the bloodstream via a line into a vein near the heart. It is expensive; the feed alone costs £150 a day – and that is without the equipment.

'He is a different child on it,' says Alison. She now has a pump at home to deliver the feed, which takes 12 hours overnight, and a special fridge to house two weeks' supply of TPN. 'I have to remember to take a bag out at 1pm so that it can warm up before I use it at 7pm. I've got an alarm clock to remind me and notes on the fridge!'

Apart from some intervening problems – Jamie's gut muscles once twisted back on themselves, another time they seized up and at one point he nearly died from a perforated bowel – Alison is hoping that Jamie can at last live his life as near to normal as it can be. He is attending school, which she hadn't expected to be possible, although he can only go for half a day at present, as he needs a nursery nurse assistant to help him. But because of his long stays in hospital, he is not used to mixing with children of his own age and Alison fears he may be a bit of an outsider.

'I noticed at the local playgroup that he didn't know how to act. He's a bit of a loner and happiest at home and with me.' She worries about how he will feel when other children notice the ways that he is different. 'They don't seem to have noticed yet but the day will come. He has an ileostomy, he is fed differently and he has a large tummy. All the bits that are wrong with him are very personal bits and that is going to be very hard for him.'

The TPN will be required for life unless a new technique to deal with the problem is developed in the future.

'With Jamie, all we can hope for is that one day bowel transplants will be possible. But that is a long way off,' says Alison. 'The main thing for us is that, at last, Jamie is happy and comfortable, he has put on weight and he has grown enormously. He is able now to enjoy his life, however different from others it is.'

Jamie has won many hearts during his long stay, including that of nurse Sarah Long.

DANIEL

While some children have problems with food because their bodies just do not function properly, with others, their difficulties – although no less severe – have more of a psychological origin. The best-known example of this type is the distressing eating disorder of anorexia nervosa, but some children can suffer from a serious dislike of food.

Four-year-old Daniel Witschi-Ray eats just yoghurt, mashed banana with sugar, jelly, ice-cream, rice pudding and an occasional biscuit with butter or cream cheese. But this is progress. Before he came on to the programme at Great Ormond Street's Feeding Clinic, he would take virtually only milk and chocolate.

Daniel is one of several children with faddy eating patterns who participate, with their parents, in a series of sessions with psychologist Mandy Bryon. The aim of this programme is not only to change the child's eating

Helping children such as Daniel overcome their fear of food is a long process, requiring determination and much patience.

habits but to alter parental attitudes which, however well meaning, might be contributing to the problem.

Daniel started to dislike food when he was nine months old, when he had a bad cold, and he never went back to eating properly again. 'We tried to open his mouth and force food into it. We'd try covering food with yoghurt on the front of the spoon, but he would just turn his head away or spit the food back at us. We tried making food look pretty. We tried camouflage. We got to the point where we just wanted to smack him, so we stopped.

'Daniel reduced himself to milk only. So we'd add powdered baby food to it and he got the nutrients he needed. And no one took our worries seriously because he wasn't underweight,' says his mother, Pearl Ray.

Pearl doesn't know what caused Daniel's aversion to food, but it has been suggested that there might have been some connection with a reflux problem – vomiting food he had eaten a couple of hours earlier – that

Daniel suffered when he was six months old.'

'The hardest thing,' she says 'is that you feel you have failed your child, whether you did or you didn't.'

Daniel also had some hearing problems and speech delay, but these are now almost corrected. However, coping with the eating problem caused friction between Pearl and Daniel's father, Thomas Witschi, while understandably, Daniel's elder sister resented having to eat foods Daniel got away with turning down. She also found it unfair not being allowed chocolate when he was allowed it freely, because it was all he would eat.

At Great Ormond Street, Pearl was reassured by blood tests that Daniel's strange eating patterns hadn't left him with any deficiencies, but his teeth had suffered and although they were not giving him pain, were removed as it was felt that they could hinder his progress in overcoming his dislike of food.

The Great Ormond Street eating programme was illuminating but hard, Pearl found.

'They videoed us having a meal of fish fingers and chips with Daniel and then analysed what was going on. I had always thought Daniel was totally uninterested in food but Mandy showed me he was. When he was turning away and I asked him to cut up his food, he turned back and did it. He also watched his dad cut up his own food.

'The big thing is that you are taught to change your attitude,' she says. 'You don't use force; you try to make meal-times fun. You try to get the child to lick foods, make teethmarks in it or touch it, because children like Daniel don't even want to go near food.'

Other important advice included finding treats to make him eat, and if he wouldn't take a food, offering smaller amounts until he did. But it is a long and painful process for everyone concerned.

'The hardest thing is finding the time and patience for all this at home and knowing there won't be big changes overnight . . . knowing, in fact, that your child might not ever completely lose a fear of food. It is also very painful for the child. We get lots of tears because Daniel really thinks that food will hurt him,' says Pearl.

She is, however, optimistic for the future. At one time, Daniel wouldn't even go near an empty plate that had had food on it. Now he'll carry the empty plates into the kitchen. And he is slowly trying more foods.

'Other people wouldn't see this as a big step forward – but it is for us.'

> *'The hardest thing is that you feel you have failed your child, whether you did or you didn't.'*
>
> **PEARL RAY,**
> DANIEL'S MOTHER

10 ORGAN TRANSPLANTS

Three types of organ transplants are carried out at Great Ormond Street: heart and heart–lung; kidney, and corneal. These are the work of three quite separate departments, but in a way all the transplant programmes suffer from a common problem: a limited supply of matching donors for the children awaiting the chance of, at the very least, a better quality of life.

A CHANGE OF HEART

In the eight years since the heart and heart–lung transplant programme began at Great Ormond Street more than a hundred children have received either a new heart, or a new heart and lungs combined. Children from all over the country, from all walks of life and social backgrounds, toddlers and young adults in their teens come to this transplant centre.

Some will have been healthy, active toddlers, leading normal children's lives and never knowing a moment of sickness until a viral infection struck without warning. The infection has passed, but its legacy persists, permanently weakening the heart muscles and shattering what was a previously healthy existence.

Many will have suffered from severe forms of cystic fibrosis, an inherited disease which affects their breathing and digestion. For them, a heart and lung or lung transplant holds out the promise of their first glimpse of freedom from a lifetime of illness. It is their chance to seize the remnants of a normal childhood.

Others awaiting transplant may have already suffered from one of the various forms of cancer. Powerful chemotherapy has saved their lives, but in the process has irreparably damaged the muscles of their heart. For them, having undergone so much already, there is still more to be endured.

For all of these children, a transplant represents, quite literally, a new lease of life. But it is a conditional offer sold without any guarantee.

'That's our biggest problem,' says Pauline Whitmore, the heart transplant team's Clinical Nurse Specialist and 'agony aunt'. 'Parents think that a heart transplant will give their child an absolute cure, and with it, a full span of life. But it doesn't.'

In reality, it offers a longer life, not necessarily a long life, a temporary injunction upon an illness which has robbed the child of the very thing it craves the most – the chance to be normal, to be like other children, no matter how short that time may be.

For children with cystic fibrosis, a successful heart and lung or lung transplant can provide relief from a blighted childhood. Once they have recovered from the operation they discover that, for the first time in their lives, breathing no longer involves a struggle. Soon too will come the realisation that it also means an end to physiotherapy four times a day, the relentless courses of intravenous antibiotics, and the embrace of a child-sized wheelchair equipped with a cylinder of oxygen.

This is the temporary but overwhelming gift which can be bestowed by taking the organs from a child who has died and giving them to another child who will live. Years of running, and playing and school-rooms and laughter, lie ahead provided the transplant goes well. But on the other hand, it may not. Some go extremely well, some go badly, but most lie in between.

Every year the transplant team must cope with the death of many of their young patients either before or after transplant. For families, assessment for the transplant programme can bring shock as well as hope: they have to accept, maybe for the first time, that their child is terminally ill. And even the hope is clouded by the fact that 60 per cent of children on the heart–lung transplant list die before they get one. Outcome of a transplant, when one does take place, is less successful than for heart transplants alone. Just half the children survive for as long as three years.

'We're still in the early development of transplantation,' says Pauline. 'Initially, when transplantation began, we felt that rejection and infection were the biggest problems. Although we still lose children from both of those, now we're better at controlling them, but other long-term problems are beginning to emerge.'

There is also the danger that the coronary arteries can become very thin and clogged, slowing the blood supply to the heart itself. Since the transplanted heart, by necessity, has had all its nerves cut, the children don't receive any warning signals or chest pains to tell them that something is wrong. The heart simply stops.

Counselling parents is a major part of Pauline Whitmore's work.

In lung transplants, a child may do extremely well after the operation, and in the months that follow. But then, for some reason, they develop a disease which slowly damages the lungs. In a short time, this new disease robs them of strength, plunging them back to the same condition which made them hope for a heart and lung transplant in the first place. In these cases, it is very difficult for children simply to accept that life has dealt them a bad hand. To them, it feels as if they have been allowed to take one bite out of the cherry, before an unseen vindictive hand takes it away.

'How much extended life a heart transplant will give a child is very much the luck of the draw. I cannot say to the parents: "Yes, your child will see their 20s, or even their late teens". When discussing the possibility of a transplant with parents, we talk in terms of five years' quality life. It's not an accurate figure, and many of our children will survive for longer periods. But it is a realistic figure, and it is easier to make correct decisions when expectations don't exceed results. Here in the transplant unit, we don't talk about quantity of life. Instead, we stress the quality.'

But for many parents, even the chance of five comparatively normal years spent with a child who has been given this lease of life becomes an easy choice to make when there may be no alternative. For all of the children who are accepted on to Great Ormond Street's transplant waiting list will have fulfilled one terrifying criterion. Each will have been judged by doctors to have less than two years left to live.

'We have two lists: a provisional list and an active list. Children who are well at the moment but who will need a heart transplant in the future go on to the provisional list. Children whose medical condition is deteriorating, and whose quality of life is falling as a result go on to the active waiting list. It depends upon what we can offer them. On the one hand we don't want to give them a heart transplant too soon, while they are still able to enjoy quality of life despite their illness. But on the other hand, we don't want to miss the boat. Some referring centres like to put their children forward for a transplant long before it is necessary.'

The stress placed upon a family waiting for their child to be called to the hospital for an organ transplant is relentless. Parents know that the telephone pager each has to carry at all times, night and day, could go off at any moment.

Instead of a sense of relief that, at last, help for their sick child is at hand, waiting for the insistent bleep saying that a donor has been found becomes an unbearable source of tension. Many find it the hardest burden to bear, harder even than their child's terminal illness. The pager raises hopes of a transplant, but it is a hope that may never be fulfilled. At least with a terminal illness there is an appalling certainty, and with time, that certainty becomes a reluctant acceptance. But the silent pager by their side removes even that tiny shred of harsh comfort.

Every morning starts with the same question: 'Could this be the one? Could this be the day my child is given the chance to lead a new life after years of illness?' It is a question the entire family may have to ask themselves each day for the best part of 18 months. And for some, it is a question which will never be answered.

No wonder all parents must undergo an assessment by the transplant team before their children are placed on the active list. It's not a selection procedure, merely a chance to weigh up how each person will cope with this pressure, to see what support they have from family and friends, and to put into place organisations and structures to plug any gaps before they are put to the test.

'Many feel guilty because their only hope is that some other child will die so that their child can live,' says Pauline. 'They feel they are not very nice people because they are wishing upon some parent the very thing that they are trying to avoid. The immense psychological effect of this burden, placed upon their shoulders for months on end, can eventually wear them down.

'That feeling often grows stronger when a heart, or heart–lung finally does become available. As well as a sense of joy, part of them will be saying: "Perhaps that accident happened because I was wishing that family bad luck."

'. . . we don't talk about quantity of life. Instead, we stress the quality.'

PAULINE WHITMORE

'I tell them that it is wrong to think that way. I tell them that, instead of feeling guilty, they should feel pleased. This transplant is bringing something positive out of the tragedy of a child's death. It is bringing life to another, and that is what the dead child's parents wanted.'

Uncertainty can also torture the cardiac team caring for a child on the waiting list whose condition is deteriorating rapidly. Inevitably, a point is reached where, to prevent further suffering, a decision must be taken to switch care away from prolonging painful life to easing the onset of an inevitable death. It's a difficult decision at the best of times, but one made harder in borderline cases. Always, there is the knowledge that a heart or lungs which could perhaps save that child's life may well become available within hours of the decision having been made.

Human organs suitable for transplant have to be in good condition, which means that most donors in this country are young people who have died from head injuries rather than prolonged illness and disease. By their very nature, children are usually well protected from life's dangers. Fewer children die from injuries that leave their organs intact, and so child donors are comparatively difficult to find. This means that every heart – and even more so, every heart and lung – is a rare commodity, placing upon the Great Ormond Street transplant team a moral duty to make the most of a scarce resource. In other words, they have to give the few organs available to the children who will get the most benefit. Deserving cases who have other diseases, or who are so ill that they won't withstand the rigours of surgery will not, by force of circumstance, be considered for transplant. There is also a psychological component to the calculation. The transplant team will assess the child to see how they will cope with the constant demands imposed by medicine, blood tests and the traumatic effect of being marked out for ever as the only kid in town with a new heart.

'It's vital that each child, no matter how young, understands to some extent what having a transplant will mean,' says Pauline. It places upon them a responsibility to adhere to a lifelong regime of medicine, and even with their parent's help this can be quite a burden to place upon young shoulders.

LOVING ENOUGH

A heart transplant was the only hope of saving one girl's life, yet still she seemed reluctant to agree. It wasn't the operation she feared, nor the thought of a strict regime of endless medicines, but something else was plainly weighing heavily on her mind. She wouldn't tell the doctors, nor any of the nurses, nor even her parents, so the job of finding out fell as usual to Pauline Whitmore.

Like all of the children awaiting transplants at Great Ormond Street, Pauline had come to know the girl very well, and now as they chatted in her room, she gradually steered the conversation around to the subject of heart transplants. She told the young girl how she would have to wait until a heart which matched her body became available, how long the operation would last, and how, after it was all over, she could lead a normal life for the first time in years. But still the young girl seemed hesitant. There seemed to have been little progress, but as the conversation came to a close, Pauline simply said to the girl: 'Are there any questions you would like to ask me?' and that's when the true reason emerged.

The girl confessed that she was worried about how she was going to feel after she had been given someone else's heart. 'I'm worried that my new heart might not love my mum and dad and brothers and sisters as much as the old one did.'

Says Pauline: 'It came as quite a shock. I had gone through all of the technical implications of a transplant, but I had forgotten one simple thing: that some children still firmly believe the heart is also the repository of all our emotions. She was afraid that someone else's heart wouldn't have the same emotions as those she had now. Out of all the dangers associated with any heart transplant, this is the one which was worrying her the most and was the cause of her reluctance.

'I suppose I shouldn't have been surprised by this little girl's literal interpretation of the word, especially when you consider how the word "heart" is used by adults in everyday language. How we love each other "from the depths of our heart" and send cards with hearts on them on Valentine's Day. In a way, it was a beautiful reminder of the innocence which separates children from adults, making them such a joy to look after.

'As well as calming her fears, I realised that my words were about to dispel a cherished myth, so I decided to tread carefully with this girl's perception of the world. Gently, I explained that the heart is just a muscle which pumps blood around the body. Although we sometimes said that we loved each other with all our heart, our emotions didn't really live there, so when she received a new heart, her feelings towards her family and friends wouldn't change one little bit.

'At first, she was dubious, and still very worried, but gradually, she began to see what I meant. Finally, I had put her fears to rest, and soon afterwards, she agreed to have a transplant. Now, she is fit and healthy, and laughs with embarrassment whenever I remind her of the discussion we had all that time ago.'

Five-year-old Danny was on Great Ormond Street's active list for a heart and lung transplant, because he suffered severely from cystic fibrosis which caused continual, severe lung infections. Sadly, Danny died before the operation could take place, but he signed his own consent form so that some of his organs could be used to save the life of another child.

AARON

Two-year-old Aaron Litchfield was Great Ormond Street's l00th child to receive a donor heart. Born perfectly healthy and with a strong heart, Aaron caught an infection at 18 months which left him very weak. Investigations revealed an enlarged heart. It had grown to three times its normal size as a result of a virus, and could no longer pump blood through his body properly. In this condition, called dilated cardiomyopathy, the heart becomes weaker and weaker.

Aaron came to Great Ormond Street from his home in Bedford where cardiologists scanned his heart and prescribed drugs but had to tell distraught parents Gail and David that, although some children recover spontaneously from these viruses, Aaron's heart wasn't recovering and a transplant within about six months was his only hope for life. Eighty-five per cent of children receiving a heart transplant are alive four years later.

'They didn't pull any punches. They told us the truth but they also did everything in their power to save my little boy,' says Gail, who also has

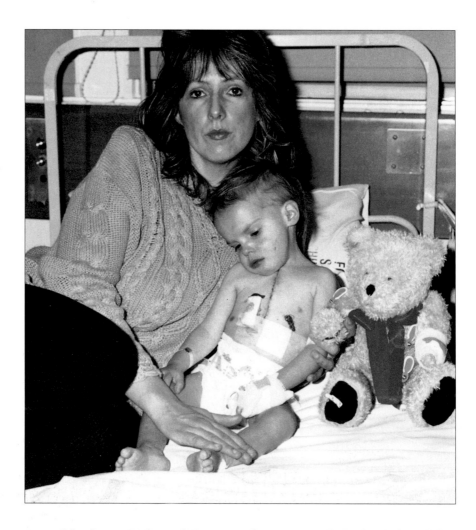

Aaron's heart had become so damaged that a transplant was his only hope for life.

two older boys, Dale and Grant, and very recently had another, Jake. Aaron was assessed for a transplant and was offered a heart a couple of months later.

For Gail it was an indescribable relief to get that call. A mother in another country whose nine-year-old daughter had just died had agreed to donate her heart and the transplant team flew there to collect it.

'Although I now had hope, some other mother had lost her child. I can never thank her enough,' says Gail.

Aaron's transplant was carried out by cardiologist Mr Marc de Leval. During the operation, Aaron's heart was connected to bypass equipment which took over the work of his heart and lungs while his own heart was removed and until the new heart was sewn in place. The whole operation lasted for five or six hours. The new heart worked well from the start. Aaron had been very lucky.

He must now take anti-rejection drugs every day of his life. At present these are in the form of a liquid, three times a day; two tablets of one kind every day and one of another kind every other day.

'I never gave up hope. And I never will,' says Gail.

'At first I was anxious about his health. But it was nine months after his transplant before he caught anything that made him poorly. And whereas it takes my others three or four days to get over a bug, I've realised it just takes Aaron a little longer. I can live with that.

'This year has been great because Aaron is back with us well and we've all been looking forward to a birth. Last year we were expecting a death.'

Gail and David will be forever grateful that everything possible was done to save Aaron's life.

HARRY

Two-and-a-half-year-old Harry Collis was the recipient of an entirely different type of transplant: a kidney. However, there was a time shortly after the transplant when his mother fervently wished they had never had it done. It wasn't a case of getting a new kidney, and then getting back to normal life. It was to be more than four agonising months after the transplant before Lesley and Simon Collis could take Harry back home with them for good.

Harry was born with both pneumonia and a hernia, which were treated at his local hospital. However, it was soon apparent that he wasn't drinking and a kidney scan two weeks later revealed that his kidneys were tiny and had stopped working properly soon after birth.

'We were immediately transferred to Great Ormond Street but I had got the impression from our local hospital that there wasn't much hope for Harry because he was too small for dialysis or a transplant,' Lesley recalls. 'But at Great Ormond Street we were told that hundreds of children had kidneys like Harry's and that they would manage him on dialysis until he could have a transplant. The doctor was surprised that we weren't more shocked. In fact we were utterly relieved because we hadn't thought he would even live!'

For the first 13 months of his life Harry was managed on drugs, then Lesley and Simon went for a two-week stay at Great Ormond Street to learn how to do his dialysis, the artificial method by which the blood is cleared of waste. It entailed connecting one end of a line to a bag of fluids attached to a dialysis machine and the other end of the line to Harry. They also had to learn how to sterilise their hands with special cream and keep them sterile during the procedure. This is vital and prevents causing life-threatening infections.

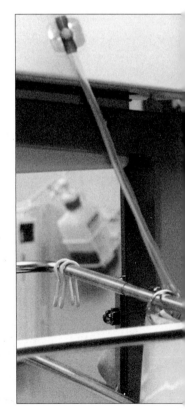

Dialysis is a big responsibility and restrictive. 'We always had to be back home by 4.30pm so that I could get him ready for dialysis and get him into bed early enough to give him 12 hours of it before he woke up. But mostly we didn't go out much anyway. Harry used to be sick a lot without warning and it was easier to stay at home, although hard on his older brother Joshua,' says Lesley.

Harry also had to be fed overnight, through a gastric tube, because of his difficulty with eating and drinking. Once he reached 10 kilograms, the magic weight, he was accepted on to the transplant programme. It was then to be 14 months before he was lucky.

Lesley remembers: 'I was watching children's television with Harry and

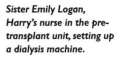

Harry and Dr John Jackman, registrar of the renal unit.

Sister Emily Logan, Harry's nurse in the pre-transplant unit, setting up a dialysis machine.

Harry's condition imposed restraints on his family's lifestyle, and sometimes the situation was particularly hard on his older brother, Joshua.

Joshua when the registrar rang, told me they had a kidney and were hoping to operate at 8am the next morning. I couldn't take it in. They wanted us to come in as soon as possible and I had to get the police to find Simon because his mobile phone didn't work. They tracked him down on the motorway and didn't mind doing it one bit.'

Once in the hospital it was an agonising wait until 4.30am before it could be confirmed that the kidney could be used for Harry. Surgeon Mr Ossie Fernando, from the Royal Free Hospital in north-west London, was to carry out the operation at Great Ormond Street.

There was then another agonising wait for the surgery to be over.

'I was sick with apprehension because I knew what it would be like afterwards, tubes and wires everywhere, and I felt so sorry for him,' says Lesley. 'But because he had been so fit and healthy before, I expected we would be home in a fortnight.'

There was a shock to come. Because the kidney was large, a great deal of fluid had had to be put into Harry's body and some had gone on to his lungs. Unable to breathe, he ended up in intensive care on a ventilator. Then he started to catch infections; this is common because of the powerful drugs that have to be used to suppress the immune system and stop it rejecting the kidney. And then his body started to reject the kidney, another normal reaction, but it took longer than expected for this to be overcome. Biopsies found nothing wrong but soon rejection occurred again, along with other complications. Harry had to go back to the operating theatre 10 times after his transplant.

'I hated that transplant then,' says Lesley. 'I just wished we had stayed on dialysis. But you can't stay on dialysis forever. I knew it was all for the best really and I was very very grateful for the donation of that kidney. Now we are home and his kidney is absolutely perfect. I am so grateful to Great Ormond Street. Recently we went away for the weekend for the first time since he was born, and it was so lovely to stay out as long as we wanted to, and not have to rush home for 4.30pm.

'There's no guarantee how long his kidney will last. I expect at some point Harry will be back on dialysis waiting for another kidney but I can't bear the thought. So we just take each day as it comes.'

A kidney transplant was to free Harry from the drudgery of dialysis, but it was four months until he could return home again.

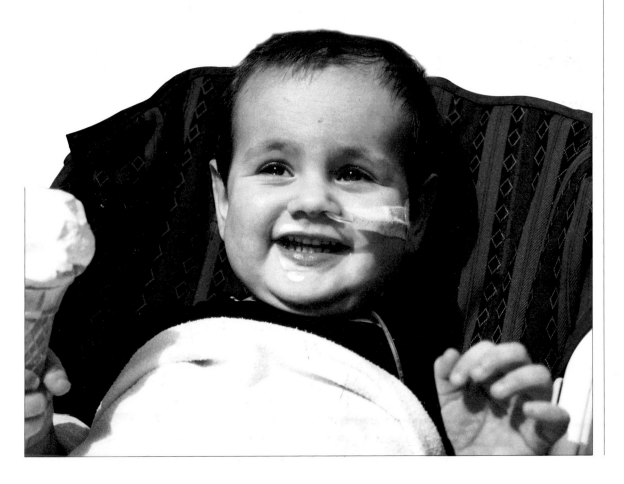

LOOKING AHEAD

While the business of running a busy hospital is more than a full-time occupation, planning for the future – both medically and business-wise – is essential. No improvement in medicine takes place without always moving forwards and trying new techniques, but the development of new ideas is almost impossible without adequate funding.

FUNDRAISING

Finding revenue over and above government-provided NHS funding is always a priority for the hospital's special trustees. It aims to raise an additional £10 million each year to provide family support services, buy the best in new equipment, and pay for further research.

A long-standing gift that continues to benefit the hospital is the play, *Peter Pan*. Its author, J M Barrie, bestowed the rights on the hospital in 1929 and the gift was confirmed in his will in 1937. Money raised all over the world from performing the play, as well as associated books, and films such as *Hook*, have benefited the hospital ever since. In 1987, when the copyright expired, Parliament voted in an amendment to the new copyright act to extend the hospital's entitlement to royalties from *Peter Pan* for as long as the hospital exists. Thus, every time someone buys a copy of the book, or goes to see a production of the play, the hospital benefits a little more.

The hospital also benefits from a whole host of other fundraising events, organised and undertaken by ordinary members of the public, that take place throughout the world. These can range from getting sponsored to run the London Marathon, cycling around Israel or climbing major mountains, to street collections, cake stalls and jumble sales.

CELEBRITY VISITORS

Many famous people, especially in the fields of sport and entertainment, have contributed to the hospital in recent years. At the forefront is Her Royal Highness the Princess of Wales. As President of the hospital, she is a regular visitor and has lent support to many aspects of hospital work.

Great excitement ensued when Hollywood stars Arnold Schwarzenegger, Danny DeVito, Emma Thompson and Julia Roberts dropped in. Not only the children, but their parents as well queued up to shake hands, request autographs and watch them pose for photographs. Closer to home, celebrities such as TV presenter Emma Forbes, actor Richard Wilson and England rugby player Rory Underwood have all lent their names to valuable fundraising and publicity initiatives. They are just a few of the hospital's many supporters

Such visits not only bring a smile to faces and provide a welcome distraction from hospital routine, but also play a valuable role in attracting publicity to the hospital, reminding the world at large that this valuable work cannot keep going without constant public support – from the most basic fundraising effort to major financial bequests.

Left: Great Ormond Street received £70,000 from the premiere night of the film Junior, which starred Arnold Schwarzenegger, Danny DeVito and Emma Thompson.

Below: Elizabeth Hurley turned on the Christmas lights in central London and met some of the children associated with Great Ormond Street, which benefited from the event.

THE CHANGING FACE OF MEDICINE

Great Ormond Street Children's Hospital and the Institute of Child Health are looking ahead. Both doctors and scientists are working together to tackle health issues facing children at the turn of the century and beyond.

Discovering new and better ways of treating children with all kinds of illnesses, both common and complex, is part of everyday life. And for children the outlook is getting brighter all the time.

For example, a great deal of work is being carried out in the field of oncology. Ten years ago, few children with leukaemia lived. Now, thanks to wider knowledge and better treatments, survival rates are vastly improved – and are getting better all the time. The hospital's epilepsy surgery programme has brought almost complete cure for children suffering from the most debilitating seizures. And heart–lung transplants, almost unheard of five years ago, are now regularly carried out.

The hospital and the Institute are also looking to generations of the future. Scientists are at the forefront in the field of paediatric genetic research – they have found the genes responsible for numerous childhood disorders and are on the way to finding some possible cures. Doctors are leading the field in detecting early signs of heart disease in children, and this exciting work could potentially help reduce the devastating problems of later life. And the whole area of pain is being studied, furthering our understanding of the ways in which children feel pain, and trying to ensure that they are as comfortable as possible when they go through medical procedures.

There is also an integrated programme of teaching and training for health-care professionals from around the country and overseas. Staff want to pass on the skills developed here so that children around the world can have the hope of a healthier future.

Great Ormond Street is very excited about its work. New developments are constantly changing and improving the face of paediatric medicine. But the story doesn't end here. There is still a great deal of work to be done to improve the health of our children, our children's children and generations beyond.

FURTHER INFORMATION

If you would like to contribute to the work of Great Ormond Street Children's Hopsital there are many ways in which you can help.

For example, you could make a donation, remember the hospital in your will, organise a fundraising event or local group activity, or enter into a covenant, which allows the Fund to claim back from the tax man an extra 33 per cent. Or perhaps you would like to know about fundraising activities in your area.

For details of these and other ways in which to support Great Ormond Street please write to:

Fundraising Department
Great Ormond Street Children's Hospital Fund
40–41 Queen Square
London
WC1N 3AJ

Volunteers
To become a volunteer at Great Ormond Street you need to be able to give at least six months' commitment. If you are interested, please write to:

Voluntary Services Department
Great Ormond Street Hospital for Children NHS Trust
Great Ormond Street
London
WC1N 3AJ

If you are planning a production of *Peter Pan*, Great Ormond Street can help with ideas and advice. Please contact:

Peter Pan Marketing Manager
Great Ormond Street Children's Hospital Fund
40–41 Queen Square
London
WC1N 3AJ

National Child Death Helpline
This helpline, run jointly by Great Ormond Sreet and the Alder Centre, attached to Alder Hey Children's Hospital in Liverpool, offers support to anyone affected by the death of a child. Answering calls are parents who have all experienced the loss of a child themselves. The helpline is staffed seven nights a week from 7pm to 10pm and on Wednesday mornings from 10am to 1pm.
The number is: Freephone 0800 282986

ACKNOWLEDGEMENTS

The authors and publisher would like to extend grateful thanks to all the children and their families who have allowed their stories to be told in this book, and to all the staff members at Great Ormond Street who so generously gave their time and support throughout its production.

Special thanks are due in particular to Polly Bide, *Great Ormond Street* series producer, and to Anna Barlow of the Great Ormond Street Press Office, without whom the book could not have been made. Sincere thanks also to producers Richard Alwyn, Jennie Cosgrove, Veronica Reinhardt, Geoffrey Smith, Viv Taylor Gee and John Farren, and to all other members of the BBC production team.

PHOTO ACKNOWLEDGEMENTS

Courtesy of Shelagh Ashley 29; Great Ormond Street Press Office 6, 8, 9, 14, 18, 92–96 (Nigel Wright), 99, 101 (Sandra Lousada) 123, 125; BBC Picture Publicity Department 24, 27, 39, 45, 53, 58, 61, 64, 67, 76, 78, 79 bottom, 86, 103 top; Piers Cavendish 7, 15, 17, 19, 26, 35, 44, 47, 51, 54, 59, 71, 81, 89, 91, 111; Press Association/Fiona Hanson 11; Lareine Shea 22, 23, 28, 30, 38, 56, 62, 68, 72, 103 bottom, 104, 105, 109, 119, 120, 121; Alan Sleator 21, 40, 74, 79 top, 83, 84, 106, 115, 116, 117; Geoffrey Smith 73; Frank Spooner Pictures 13.